# Through
# Charley's Door

*Books by Emily Kimbrough*

\* \* \*

OUR HEARTS WERE YOUNG AND GAY
(with Cornelia Otis Skinner)

WE FOLLOWED OUR HEARTS TO HOLLYWOOD

HOW DEAR TO MY HEART

IT GIVES ME GREAT PLEASURE . . .

THE INNOCENTS FROM INDIANA

THROUGH CHARLEY'S DOOR

# Through Charley's Door

BY

## EMILY KIMBROUGH

*Drawings by Alice Harvey*

HARPER & BROTHERS    PUBLISHERS    NEW YORK

*Library of Congress catalog card number: 51-11929*

*To*
*ACHSAH GARDNER KIMBROUGH*
*With Love*

# ACKNOWLEDGMENT

Lloyd Lewis, the distinguished American historian, interviewed seventy-five Marshall Field employees who had served the organization many years. Perhaps he had in mind writing a book about the store and the people in it, but Mr. Lewis died suddenly in 1949.

After his death, Mrs. Lewis, going over his papers, found the collection of interviews and gave it to Marshall Field & Company for its research library. I have used some of this material.

My gratitude to Mrs. Lewis for making it available is deep, and my appreciation of Mr. Lewis' craftsmanship more than I can express adequately without being fulsome. I regret that because this volume had to be contained within the frame of personal recollection, I could bring to these pages only portions of the Lewis interviews with Charley, Miss Bredin and Miss Duggan.

My thanks go herewith, also, to the executives of Marshall Field & Company, because they gave me access to any and all material I might wish for this book, and particularly because they did not so much as glance over my shoulder to learn what use was being made of it.

# Through
## Charley's Door

# * 1 *

LATE IN the winter of 1923, I acknowledged to her, and—what was harder—to myself, that my chum, Cornelia Otis Skinner, was an actress. Together we had gone to Paris in the spring and studied there with an actor of the Comédie Française, Monsieur Dehelly. Cornelia's purpose in this had been to learn the technique of the French Theater. Mine—and she was careful to point this out to him when she applied for permission to include me—to better my French. My knowledge of the language was not spectacularly increased by these lessons, but I did exchange my native Hoosier accent when speaking French for one that persists to this day and that Cornelia maintains is certainly not French, but has the peculiar distinction of bearing no relation to any tongue she has ever heard. The only talent I had brought to the French Drama was a quick memory and the facility for learning lines, though my interpretation of them had left everything to be desired.

Cornelia had been slower to learn, but Monsieur Dehelly had commended her every speech. When I had rendered for him an entire role from the first through the last act, he had kept the book open and followed, with his finger and a furrowed brow, each line as I spoke it.

That had been in the late summer of 1923. In November we were back in America, I in Chicago because I lived there, and she in Chicago because she had a part in a play. The play was called *Bristol Glass* and it was produced at the Blackstone Theater.

Cornelia was an actress, and I, as far as I could see, was going to be nothing at all. I was at the moment in the theater myself, but I could not, even to Cornelia, elaborate my appearances there to a recognition on her part, or anyone's, that we were comparably on the stage. I performed only every Saturday in the morning, and in the company of other members of the Junior League giving plays for children at the Studebaker Theater; no dramatic critics, in fact very few Chicago citizens over the age of ten, witnessed my interpretations of *The Tin Woodman* or *Puss in Boots*. When in December the Junior League expanded its theatrical activities to a musical extravaganza in two acts and two performances at the Auditorium, I was put in the chorus.

By the end of the run of the extravaganza, its second performance, I faced the future with a cold, clear acceptance that Cornelia and I had come to a parting of careers, and that there was one other sizable difference between us. I had no career at all.

Cornelia was the only one of my friends who had stepped out on her own. The others were happily at home or getting ready to leave by the conventional exit, marriage. One or two of them had experienced an urge to stand on her own by holding down a job, but the urge had been quickly stamped out by family disapproval. This inclination on the part of daughters was a favorite topic of conversation among parents in 1923. When the subject was broached at any social gathering in our house, I had invariably an impulse to clap my hand over my mother's mouth or in some way distract her from voicing the sentiments I knew were hers and hers alone.

Other mothers would say, "I can't imagine what has got into young girls nowadays. You send them to college and they come back discontented with their homes. What is the matter with home, I would like to know. I certainly enjoyed mine. Why can't they do charity work and be useful citizens, instead of this craze to earn money of their own? Selfish, I consider it."

What mother considered it was a far different thing and she never failed to say her opinion aloud. "Natural, understandable, and commendable" were some of the words she used. "Ignorant, benighted, sentimental" comprised a few of the epithets she applied to her friends, and their opinions.

"Every girl," this was one of her favorite outbursts and most frequently repeated, "should have the capacity to earn her own living. To be economically independent is the only way I know for a woman to become mentally independent. She'll never know whether or not she's able to have this independence unless she practices it. If we didn't want our daughters to exercise their minds, we should never have allowed them to become literate." These were among mother's public declarations of her point of view. In private she expanded her theme with the information that though I would be fed, housed and clothed, whatever I wanted or needed above the bare necessities—and very bare, she invariably stressed—would have to come of my own providing, particularly because of the principle of the thing, and partly because the family could not afford any more. Bird life made one of mother's favorite examples. "When the time comes," she always illustrated this with a violent gesture of heave-ho, "the parents push the little ones out of the nest."

I am not quick at catching a hint, but I did gather that in mother's opinion the Kimbrough nest was becoming crowded.

Since no mother I knew was sympathetic to the opinion of mine, I went to see a spinster friend of the family's, Miss Etheridge. I told her I didn't want the family to know anything of my plan, because I would probably meet opposition. My mother didn't approve of girls' stepping out on their own, I said. I felt reasonably sure this maiden lady had not participated in any of the conversations pertaining to daughters, and had no intention of revealing to her that I was edged to the rim of my home and barely hanging on. Instead, I assured her I was a girl with high ambition.

Miss Etheridge was impressed. Ambition was an admirable trait, she declared, and I should not be ashamed of it. She would help me further it and stand beside me in the face of any family opposition.

A few days after this gratifying conversation, she telephoned and, though I assured her mother was not at home, whispered over the wire that she had talked with a young woman she knew who had a job at Marshall Field's in the Advertising Department. Her name was Achsah Gardner, and she would see me the following morning at nine-thirty o'clock in her office on the ninth floor of Marshall Field's retail store. I thanked her, in a whisper too, since she evidently wanted the conversation on that tone, and promised to let her know the outcome of my interview.

I broke the news to mother on the following morning about eight-thirty. Mother was at her desk in the living room; I saw her as I went down the hall, but I didn't speak to her until I was at the front door. With my hand on the knob, I called back, "I'm on my way in town. I'm going to try for a job."

"Hurray!" Mother answered, and added loudly, "Remember, with your shield or on it."

I was glad Miss Etheridge was not beside me.

The sentiment about the shield was an old battle cry of mother's, and had been used to send me out on every trial of strength from the first day of school to Bryn Mawr examinations. She meant every word of it. I was never in doubt of that.

When she voiced this slogan I was out of her sight, and deliberately. I did not want her to suggest any changes in my armor. I had selected for my interview a dress I had made in Paris. I had made only one and it had turned out to be unusual. This was largely due to the fact that I had selected a material, for reasons not clear to myself, that was, I think, designed for a couch cov-

"I'm on my way to town. I'm going to try for a job."

ering—heavy velour with a raised pattern, in dull gold. My intention had been to copy a model I'd bought at a sale of Jenny's. I'd laid the Jenny dress on top of the material and sheared around it, but no one had ever explained about seams and making allowances for them. When the seams of my dress were sewn, I could get into the garment only by easing it down over my figure, as if I were putting a case on an umbrella. The only adornment I'd permitted was a belt I'd bought at the Galeries Lafayette. It was of heavy metal representing silver, studded with large, very imitation turquoises. Since my shape at that time was very akin to that of an umbrella, it afforded no natural resting place for the belt. Loops had proved to be impractical because the weight of the belt sagging on them pulled out the seams at those points where the loops were sewn, and each restitching of the seams made the dress a little tighter. Left unsupported, the belt, without any warning, would coast rapidly to the ground, shackling me.

I had learned to forestall this ignominy by inserting a thumb under the belt and resting my hand on one hip. Since this was the position affected by the models I had seen parading in the Salon of a big dressmaker where I had been taken once by a stylish friend, I had quite a fancy for the stance, even unprompted by necessity. I told myself in the mirror that walking this way made me look very blasé.

I had not as yet found an occasion ripe for displaying the walk nor the dress to my parents. But applying for a job at Marshall Field's seemed to me a very ripe occasion.

The dress had no sleeves, because I did not know how to make them, but I was happy in the addition to my costume of very short gloves. The combination of short or no sleeves and short gloves had just come into style in Paris. I hoped to surprise Marshall Field's with it.

The hat that accompanied this costume was of golden velvet with a dark brown ostrich plume curled round the crown. I'd bought it in Paris at a little shop not far from our Pension and, encouraged by the proprietress, added a veil, cream color with large brown spots. I tied this very tight over my face, because it seemed to me that to have my eyelashes caught in its meshes was seductive. The end of my nose, however, caught the brunt of this pressure, and carried for some time after the veil was removed a conspicuously indented ring.

My pocketbook for this costume was beige suède, with a large medallion of enamel to mark the clasp. My shoes were beige suède too, pale and with exceptionally high heels.

Over this ensemble I was forced to wear to Field's my old muskrat coat, but I planned to leave this at the checking counter immediately inside the Washington Street entrance to the store.

It did not occur to me that mother would not like the costume; I was only afraid she might consider it too dressy for 8:30 A.M., a point of view I held to be old-fashioned. I was dressed, and suitably dressed, I felt, for an occasion; the hour was an unimportant detail. I didn't wish to argue this with her, nor did I care for her to see that I was taking my dog along. My dog had come from Paris too. His name was Gamin, and he was a Brussels griffon, weighing not more, I think, than seven pounds; beige, too. He had looked wistful at being left behind, but would look effective, I'd decided quickly, in the crook of the arm that supported my belt.

We got out the door safely, but I kept him under my coat until we were well out of sight of the living-room windows, just in case mother should come there to wave me off, a custom of hers when she sent me on a "With your shield . . ." undertaking. I got the Electric out of the garage in back of our apartment building, put Gamin on the seat, but covered him by a fold of my coat. We went out the driveway and past our apartment. I opened the window, craned my head out to look up at our apartment on the third floor. Mother was at a living-room window, waving. She tapped sharply on the glass when she saw my head, but I didn't stop. I pulled the steering bar toward me, turned right, and headed for downtown Chicago.

Gamin sat beside me, released from under my coat. He looked up at me while I said aloud the speeches I was planning for the interview. "I think I would like to be in your Book Department. I like to read and I read very quickly. I would be delighted to write Book Reviews that you could print in your advertisements in the newspapers."

This sounded competent, I decided. After practicing it several times with variations, my mind was at ease, though physically I seemed unable to quiet the trembling of my hand on the steering bar, or the thumping of my heart under the gold velour.

I put the Electric in Grant Park and walked Gamin on the leash to the store. I planned to place him under my arm at the checking counter after I had deposited my coat. My belt, at the moment, was secured by a large safety pin attached to the coat lining. I planned to leave the pin, too, with the coat.

We waited on the corner of Washington and Wabash Avenues for the policeman to blow his whistle twice, the signal for east and west traffic to pass, and I looked across at the store of Marshall Field's stretching the whole block from Washington to Randolph, and all the way around to State Street. It seemed bigger than I had thought it to be. I remembered the first time I had seen it. That had been after we had moved to Chicago from Muncie, Indiana, and mother and father had taken Brother and me to the Toy Department on the fourth floor, and lunch in the Tearoom on the seventh. It had been one of the most exciting days in my life, but I didn't remember my knees shaking then. They were shaking now.

The policeman blew his whistle twice. The second note of a Chicago policeman's whistle always drops a little, making it almost a third sound. "WHEE, whee-whee" was the way my young brother imitated it.

Gamin and I moved out from the curb with the crowd.

Charley, the doorman, was on duty as always at the Washington Street entrance. He and I had become friends because he knew so many of my friends who had been born in Chicago, and their mothers and even the grandmothers of some of them. He smiled when he saw Gamin and me, and said good morning.

"That's a mighty cute little fellow," he added, clucking his

fingers down at Gamin. "Some of your friends are in today." He gave me the news as usual. "Miss Donnelley's up on the fifth floor looking for a hat. She said to tell any of you that came in she'd be in the Narcissus Room at one o'clock for lunch—regular table."

"I'm not here for shopping today." When I said this my tongue seemed to get thick and heavy in my mouth. Swallowing took a little time before I could speak again. "I'm going to try to get a job here," I said, "at Field's."

My friend nodded his head. "Well, God be with you and bring you luck. You'll never regret working here to the longest day you live."

Gamin and I went through Charley's Door.

## * 2 *

CHARLEY AND I had been introduced to each other by a school friend of mine in about 1912, not long after my family had moved from my birthplace, Muncie, Indiana, to Chicago. In 1923 Charley had been doorman at the Washington Street entrance of Field's for about thirty-three years. A weekly pay envelope carried his full name, Charles F. Pritzlaff. He'd shown it to me one time, but I doubt that half a dozen people in the store, nor many of the customers he served, would have known who Mr. Pritzlaff was. And yet every member of that branch of Chicago society, called reverently in the store, "The Carriage Trade," knew Charley, and named the entrance over which he presided, "Charley's Door."

You could enter the store by way of Wabash Avenue, Randolph, or State Streets, but if you chose the Washington Street entrance—and the Carriage Trade chose it—you were at Charley's Door. If you happened to go in or out by one of the other doors, that was only a convenient passageway at the moment. To go by Charley's was to enjoy a social interlude, and at the same time benefit by a special service that was his own and was a symbol, perhaps, of what made Marshall Field's different from other department stores.

Charley greeted you by name and told you who of your

The Carriage Trade chose Charley's Door.

friends were shopping at the moment in the store. He took and delivered messages or parcels for his patrons; a book one of them wanted to lend to a friend, an umbrella left behind at a house and restored more easily through Charley than from one dwelling to the other. Distances in Chicago are wide, social exchange between the North and South Sides involves considerable traveling, but Charley's Door was a middle ground. Frequently, a Field customer in a hurry for merchandise would order it by telephone and have the parcel delivered to Charley with instructions for him to engage a taxi and give the parcel to the driver, who would be paid by the lady at the place of delivery.

Charley was of medium height and build, with a long, thin nose, and small, sharp, but friendly eyes that lighted up instantly a customer came into his view. His memory for faces and the name that went with each one was amazing and a source of considerable pride to him. He developed and perfected this talent by constant practice. He always asked courteously the name of each new customer who came his way, and when he had seen her through his Door, he would write it down.

The third or fourth time my mother and I came his way to Field's, he'd said, "Good morning, Mrs. Kimbrough." Mother, pleased and startled, had asked how in the world he had remembered her name. Every night, he'd told her, he read over the list of new customers collected that day and as he memorized it, went over in his mind the appearance of the owner of each name.

"Sometimes," he'd said and chuckled, "I surprise out-of-town customers by calling their name when perhaps they haven't been to the store in four or five years." He had a list of out-of-town customers alone, he'd confided, that ran into the hundreds. He didn't always, he'd explained, ask a person outright, for fear he might be considered fresh. Sometimes he'd take down the license number of the car and then look up the owner's name.

Charley's Door was the favorite meeting place for the young. Waiting there one day for a friend, long before I had thought of having a job at Field's, I'd asked Charley what he had done before he came to Field's. Someone had told me he'd been a butler.

"No," he'd said, "I was a coachman for Mr. F. J. Kennett. He lived at Ontario and St. Clair, and was a broker. Mr. Gordon Selfridge lived not far away with his mother. He was General Manager of Field's then. That was before he went to London and opened a store. I guess he used to see me. They had Horse Shows at the Exposition Building where the Art Institute is now. I showed Mr. Kennett's horses there and one year we took two Blue Ribbons in a row. It wasn't long after that, I remember, Mr. Selfridge recommended me to Mr. Field for a doorman. There was only one other doorman in town, at H. V. Walker's Dry Goods Store. Mr. Selfridge persuaded Mr. Field it would be snappy to have a doorman who knew society people."

I'd asked him then if a doorman's was a better job than a coachman's.

"Easier," he'd told me. "We had nice uniforms, though. They matched the upholstery of the carriage. In summer we wore white buckskin breeches and boots, with silk hats. We were a lot better dressed than chauffeurs are today."

I'd wanted to know what he had worn as a doorman when he started.

"I had a silk hat, but a cap was more practical, and I got them to let me change. Otherwise it was just a regular uniform."

Another day I'd asked Charley if the hours had been better in the beginning as a doorman than they had been as a coachman.

"Much better," he'd told me, "even though I worked seven days a week here. I took the watchman's place on Sundays and walked around outside the building; on holidays, too. Of course I don't do that any more. The store opened at eight then, and closed at five-thirty. But I had my nights at home."

Once when I was waiting for a friend to pick me up in her car Charley said, "Automobiles have made people rude. It's taken

[ 16 ]

all the high tone out of them. They aren't polite to each other, and they aren't so polite to service people as the people in horse carriages were."

I asked how it had been in the carriage days. He smiled happily and closed his eyes for a moment in reminiscent pleasure.

"A lady would drive up, I'd help her out, and then the coach-man would find a position anywhere from State to Michigan. Sometimes carriages would line up these two blocks double rows. If people drove their own buggies, they would hitch the horses to rings in the pavement, but the coachmen didn't. They just sat on the coachman seats, they were called 'dickey seats,' and watched for me to give the sign that their mistress was ready to go.

"A good many of the women had their maids with them.

There'd be a time, most likely, when I could get to talk to the maid. Coachmen didn't talk. They weren't supposed to. It was a disgrace for a society lady to have a discussion with her coachman. He'd take his orders from her with his eyes straight ahead and his hand at salute and wouldn't even nod that he understood. There's no style like that now. Ladies sit inside an automobile and talk to the chauffeur, have regular conversations with them.

"In the old carriage days society ladies had the shopping habit, you might say. I guess they didn't have so much else to do. Many of them would drive down to Field's every day. They were too high-toned to carry packages. The store had boys who carried them out. I'd whistle for the carriage and it would drive up. All the coachmen would be watching, and I'd know where every lady's carriage would be standing. I'd keep it in mind when I was walking up and down. Of course Field's was exclusively the store for society people. Why, there was one street cleaner kept busy working all day long, up and down in front of this store. It was the only place in the city where one cleaner had only one block to care for, carriages double-parked, and two horses to each carriage. You never saw our ladies hurrying to get in or out of a carriage. A real lady wouldn't budge until I'd open the door and lift back the robe. Then she'd speak pleasant to me and I'd speak nice to her."

My friend's car came up to the curb. Charley and I walked across the sidewalk to it. "Take women in automobiles," he added. "Most of them open the door themselves and pile out. You try and help some women out of an automobile today, and they jump. They act as if they thought they'd done something wrong."

He opened the door for me. "Good morning, Miss Donnelley," he said, recognizing instantly my friend at the wheel. "Your grandmother's in the store today. I'll tell her I saw you and that you're looking just fine."

Eleanor Donnelley leaned across me to hand Charley a package. "How are you, Charley?" she said. "Would you mind giving

[ 18 ]

my grandmother this package? Tell her it's a pattern she wanted
from my mother. We knew she'd be here today. She said on the
telephone this morning she was going shopping."

Charley took the package. "Drive carefully now," he cautioned
as we pulled out, "in this crazy traffic nowadays—with no manners in anybody any more."

Had Charley carried a banner, "politeness" would have been the
word written on it. He didn't display this quality obsequiously, but
he exercised it consistently from the arrival of the first customer
in the morning until the last had departed. Sometimes the departure would be an hour or more after the store had closed.
If a customer's carriage, and later, motor car, were waiting outside his door, Charley knew the customer was still shopping
inside, and if she had not come out by the time the store closed,
Charley waited until she did emerge, to show her into her con-
veyance, carry her bundles for her, and wish her good evening.

Charley was as sensitive to the quality of politeness in others
as a hunting dog to a whiff of quail and, like a hunting dog,
stiffened to pleased and rapt attention when he encountered it.
To have that one quality was, in Charley's opinion, sufficient
endowment for any human being. He himself did not feel the
need of any others to accompany it. And so wherever he encountered that virtue, he was pleased with the individual who
possessed it.

He did not tell me, and certainly he did not tell my mother,
but he confided to Mr. Lloyd Lewis, the historian, and I had it
directly from him, that some of the politest people who came to
Charley's Door, and so among the finest in his estimation, were
the "Madames."

"They brought their girls with them sometimes," Charley had
confided to Mr. Lewis, "and the girls were just as polite and well-
behaved as their Madames. Nobody ever knew who they were
but me, I guess. The Eversleigh sisters came a good deal, and also
Carrie Watson and Mrs. Frankie Wright, and Vic Shaw. They

liked me. Of course I treated them like everybody else, better than some, because you couldn't have asked for nicer manners. Once Frankie Wright gave me a two-dollar ticket to a Catholic Church bazaar. She gave it to me very graciously. I often wondered how she happened to get it. They were very goodhearted," Charley assured Mr. Lewis. "Why," he said, "once I was calling Carrie Watson's carriage for her. An old tramp passed and what do you think she said? 'Charley,' she said to me, 'here, give this half-dollar to that poor old man.' And I did. She was a kind woman."

Once Charley said to me, "I've always looked at it that my job is to be the same to everybody. That way everybody feels Marshall Field's has been polite, and Marshall Field's has always treated me fine. They've never docked me once when I was sick. They talk a lot about the quality of Field merchandise, but I think they put a lot of quality into treating people."

I went into Field's by Charley's Door on the day I applied for a job because I wanted his good wishes and something of his quality behind me.

# * 3 *

AT THE checking desk on the first floor I asked the location of the Advertising Department from the girl who took my coat. I asked her while I was undoing the safety pin that had secured my belt, fastening the pin to the lining, adjusting my thumb through my belt to hold it in place, my hand on my hip, and then arranging my dog under that arm. She evidently didn't hear me. I had to ask twice, "Can you tell me where the Advertising Department is?"

Even then she only gave a start and said, "Pardon?" though she was only the width of the counter away and looking at me very intently, at least at my belt and Gamin.

I asked a third time; then she told me she didn't know. This annoyed me a little but she pleased me almost immediately after, by asking if I were a foreigner. When I hurried away carrying Gamin, she was standing, holding my coat, making no move to put it on a checking rack.

The Advertising Bureau was on the ninth floor, an elevator operator told me. The minute I stepped out, I realized I had never before been on the ninth floor.

In front of me was an entrance to a large room, in which, as far as I could see, no merchandise of any sort was displayed. There was a luxurious gray carpet on the floor, there were some chairs here and there in pairs with a small table between each pair, and at the back of the room two handsome folding screens. This was just as I had imagined an Advertising Department would look—"a room of quiet elegance." I'd seen that phrase frequently in Marshall Field advertising.

I stepped through the doorway. A woman in black taffeta of quiet elegance rustled to me from a far corner of the salon, and asked in a voice of Q.E. if she could be of assistance.

"I'm looking for the Advertising Department," I told her, and wondered if, trying again, I could make my speech sound refined, like hers. I couldn't. When I added, "I have an appointment with Miss Gardner," my enunciation sounded as if I'd bitten into a lemon.

"This," said Pearly Tones, "is Section Twenty-eight, the Custom Apparel Department. The Advertising Bureau," she pointed a long, drooping, aristocratic finger, "is down there, I believe."

I thanked her and departed hastily in the direction she had indicated. Either I was too nervous to be able to follow a finger, or the languorous curve of hers put me off the path, because I got into the Household Utilities Section and, from there, the Bed Department.

The ninth floor also contained the Executive Offices, housing the President, Vice-President, etcetera. Mercifully, as I passed them, I was spared that knowledge. Emerging from the Beds, I was vaguely aware only of a long space, something like a large pen, because of a low railing that separated it from the aisle. It seemed to contain three or four desks, empty, save one, where a young man sat writing.

As I passed him a bell rang, he got up and went to a large, solid, dark wood door at the back of the pen, opened it, and I suppose walked into the room beyond. At the moment, however, my attention was fixed on an inconspicuous sign ahead of me reading, ADVERTISING BUREAU.

The offices of the Advertising Department were behind a solid wood counter more than waist high. Standing at the counter I could see through open doorways into three offices. A door beside me at the end of the counter was the only one closed. It had a somewhat odd appearance, because though the side away from me was set in a partition or wall as high as the door itself, the side nearer me was only in its own frame above the counter. Inside it, between the counter at which I stood and the offices I could look into, ran a long table about three feet wide and at least the length of the three offices. There was an aisle on either side of the table. On my side there was enough space in the aisle for a desk.

No one was at this desk, but several people were standing at the long table, men and girls, perhaps five or six in all. They were bending over sheets of newspaper and they were talking. Occasionally, as I watched, one would attack a news sheet with a pencil, draw a line violently from somewhere on the page to the margin, write rapidly and in big letters, and then make a circle around what was written.

A young man stood a little apart from the others. He was peeling cut-out figures from a page. I saw him turn these cut-outs over, brush them with a thick colorless kind of glue from a big jar beside him, and replace them in a different position on the page.

They were all obviously in a great rush. A heavy-set man among them with red hair was talking into a telephone that stood on the table in the midst of the newspaper sheets. Above the other voices I couldn't hear what he was saying. But occasionally he would point with his free hand to something on the page, and one of the other people would stop talking and nod an agreement.

This was the worst possible moment, I decided, to apply for a job. Field's was in a crisis. On the other hand, I had a specific appointment with Miss Gardner. If I didn't let her know I was there, she would probably, I thought, refuse another time to be bothered with me should I get up enough courage to telephone for a second appointment.

While I was trying to justify my impulse to walk as rapidly as possible to the nearest exit, a boy came into my view from around the corner inside. Evidently there were more offices in the department than I could see. The boy sat down at the desk directly in front of me across the counter. He couldn't help seeing me since my head was just over his, but he paid no attention to me. He wrote something on a memorandum pad.

Since no one was paying any attention to me, I considered the expedience of sinking slowly to my knees out of sight beneath the counter and departing inconspicuously on all fours. Then no one would have to notice me and I would be happier by far than I was at the moment. As my head was easing down slowly out of sight, the boy spoke without looking up from his writing.

"Did you want to see someone?" he said.

I regained my full stature with a jerk. "Miss Gardner," I told him, and this time my voice squeaked, "I have an appointment with her."

"Just a minute," he answered, and left his desk. He walked out of sight around the corner. I wanted to be out of sight too, but I held on to the counter.

Presently he came back, followed by a pretty young woman. My general uneasiness seemed to have blurred my vision. I couldn't see her features clearly; well enough, however, to note she had eyes that were nearly yellow. And I thought to myself, "I don't think I've ever before seen topaz eyes except on a cat."

The boy stepped to one side, she came forward, and shook hands with me over the counter. "You're Emily Kimbrough, aren't you?" she said.

I smiled, nodded, and took her hand. I thought I wouldn't try my voice again, just yet.

"Will you come into my office?"

The boy pushed a button under the counter on his side. The

door to my left, that was in a solid frame only on one side, clicked at the knob. I pushed it, and walked in. I had to squeeze past the people at the center table, but none of them noticed.

Miss Gardner led the way into an office next to and just around the corner from the far one I had been able to see. She sat down at her desk and indicated for me to sit in a chair beside her.

"I think I'd better come at another time," I said.

Miss Gardner's eyebrows rose. "Why?" she asked.

I turned my head in the direction of the knot of agitated people I had just skirted. "Something's happened, hasn't it?" I asked.

She leaned forward to look, and laughed while she explained that what I saw was the daily proofreading of the newspaper advertising, a rush to make the deadline. "It will all be over in a few minutes," she added.

We came around then to talking about me and what I wanted to do. First we talked about Paris, because her friend and my sponsor, Miss Etheridge, had told her I had been there only a few months before. Miss Gardner had lived in Paris as a child and had gone to school there. She told me a little about that, but broke off to ask if I had got my clothes in Paris, adding she hoped I didn't mind her asking since fashion was her business, and my costume was one she hadn't seen before. I assured her happily I didn't mind in the least and that my clothes had come from Paris. I thought it unnecessary to elaborate that the dress had not come from any of the big houses but from the floor of my bedroom at the Pension where I had cut it out.

It had been apparent to me from the very outset of our interview that Miss Gardner was interested in my costume, could in fact scarcely take her eyes from it. I accepted with a glow of pleasure this endorsement of my selection. But when she said she supposed I wanted to write fashion copy I was startled. In the first place I didn't know what the word "copy" meant. Furthermore, the idea of writing had not crossed my mind, except per-

[ 25 ]

haps to do book reviews as a corollary to selling that merchandise. When I told her this she was as surprised as I had been at her suggestion. She had nothing to do, she explained, with selling in the store, and had supposed since I'd come to the Advertising Bureau I wanted a job in advertising.

I rearranged in my mind my career while she said this, and assured her when she had finished that advertising was what I had really wanted. I was a little dazed, after having said this, picturing myself caught up in the hurly-burly just then subsiding at the table outside, and so I didn't take in the details clearly of Miss Gardner's next sentences. They had to do with a Clara Wilson who had edited a magazine published by Field's, but had recently gone to New York to be Art Editor of *Harper's Bazaar*. In consequence, Miss Gardner had moved from newspaper advertising, was taking over the magazine; someone else was being moved into another position.

But I did clearly hear her say, "And so I'll give you an assignment and then we'll see. Excuse me a minute." She got up from her seat at the desk and left the office.

I sat in rigid suspense like someone posing for a flashlight picture, but my mind was careening around and up a ladder of successful journalism until I was perched on the top rung, directing all the advertising in all the newspapers of Chicago, possibly of America. Gamin jumped on my lap, but I hadn't noticed, until Miss Gardner, returning, stooped over and tickled him behind an ear. "I'm afraid," she said, "if you come here to work, Marshall Field & Company will not welcome a dog with you."

I came down the ladder rapidly, stammering that I always left Gamin behind. Today was an exception.

If this gave Miss Gardner the impression I was an old hand at holding jobs, with or without a dog, she gave no indication of it. She was carrying a sheet of paper. She sat down at her desk and showed the paper to me. "This is a requisition," she explained, "from Section Twenty-eight for a story in tomorrow's *Tribune* on a costume they are designing. Mary McCormick is to wear it at her debut next week in the opera, *The Snowbird*." She swung her chair around and pointed; her finger was short and straight. "Section Twenty-eight is the Custom Apparel Department. It's over there at the far end of the store. Mr. McNab is the head of it. Ask him to show you the sketches for the costume, and get anything else from him he can tell you. You may have to do some research on your own. Write up the story and let me have it." She handed me the paper.

"I understand," I told her. And that was as false a statement as I had ever made in my life.

Miss Gardner stood up, and that this indicated the end of our interview was the only thing I had understood during the preceding five minutes. She took the paper from my hand, folded it, put it in an envelope and gave it back to me.

I slid Gamin to the floor, stood up, shook hands with her and moved out of her office past the table, cleared now of people and newspaper sheets.

"Good luck," she called after me.

Later, reviewing in my mind the interview step by step, I could not remember answering her. But I did ask the office boy who was at his desk again to let me out.

"Just turn the knob and open the door," he said. "It's only locked from the other side to keep out the Buyers."

When I came to this statement in my later reviewing, I could make no more sense of it than when the office boy said it. What things people came to the Advertising Department to buy I couldn't imagine, nor why they had to be kept out.

There was, I felt sure, a direct route from the Advertising to the Custom Apparel Section, but I wasted no time experimenting; there was more important work to be done. I retraced the ground I'd covered, past the large space, like a pen, where I saw the young man I'd noticed on the trip in. He was at his desk, looked up in a friendly way and I essayed a slight nod, hoping this would indicate I was a fellow member now of Marshall Field & Company. I whisked through Beds, Household Utilities, and was once more in the Custom Apparel room. Q.E. was lolling elegantly in a chair. She did not rise at the sight of me, but closed her eyes wearily and asked, "Haven't you found the Advertising Department?" She opened her eyes with an effort.

"Oh, yes," I assured her briskly. She couldn't intimidate me, now that I knew her salon was called by those in the know, just Section 28, and was run by a man named McNab. "I found it. I'm working for it. I have a request from your department for a story. May I see Mr. McNab?"

That brought her up on her feet, with a hasty, "Why, certainly. I'll get him."

It sent me sagging, however, into the chair she quit, unmuscled by my bold talk and my anxiety over what to say to Mr. McNab. If this figure of refinement was only a saleswoman, Mr. McNab was probably, I decided, a member of an impoverished branch of some royal house in Europe working incognito.

Mr. McNab was a short, stocky Scotsman. He came into the quiet, dimly lighted room calling, "Hello, hello there." (He pronounced it, "Halloo, halloo.") "You were wanting to see me?"

Miss Pearly Tones swayed in behind him. Before I could get up from my chair he had dropped his not inconsiderable bulk into the one beside me. He reached, without asking, for the envelope I was holding, opened it, and read the paper inside.

"That's right," he told me when he had come to the end of it. He read slowly, forming every word with his lips. When he spoke, he clung to each "r." "Now what can I tell you?"

He couldn't tell me much, I found. "It's genu*ine*," he said. But genuine what, was not clear to him. "I know verra little about these fine clothes of ours," he admitted apologetically, with a wave of his hand, thick and stubby, around the gray salon. "Figures, and by that I mean numbers," he slapped a hand on his knee in enjoyment of his joke, "that kind of figures is my line.

[ 28 ]

And I'll tell you another thing. Wherever there's big money coming in at Marshall Field's, you'll always find a Scotsman in charge. This section is called '28' because the address of Charley's Door is 28 Washington Street. That's where the carriage trade comes in, and this is the section it comes to."*

After I left Mr. McNab, I went downstairs to Charley. I told him the news I had been given work to do, and asked if he would keep Gamin for me while I "covered an assignment," a phrase I remembered from an O. Henry story.

Charley congratulated me and tethered Gamin inside the door.

After stopping at the Stationery Department on the first floor to buy a notebook and some pencils, I went to the Art Institute, the Library, and the Historical Society. Around two o'clock I bought some sandwiches, went back to the store, and gathered up Gamin. We ate together in the Electric at Grant Park. After lunch I brought Gamin to Charley again, and went on with my work. I wrote my story at a desk in the Public Library over on Michigan Avenue, and then took it to my father's office to have it typed. My father was out but his secretary, Miss Dennis, said she'd be delighted to help me.

The piece turned out to fill three typewritten pages, single space, and it wasn't finished until after five. I ran with it all the way back, nine blocks from my father's office, but when I came in sight of the big Marshall Field clock at the corner of State and Washington, I saw it was after five-thirty. I knew the store would be closed and I began to cry a little in despair. But I kept on running.

Charley was waiting for me, walking Gamin up and down the sidewalk in front of his Door. He hadn't the authority to let me in, he said, but he promised to deliver my story himself, and immediately, to the Advertising Bureau, care of Miss Gardner. Gamin and I went home.

Mother hurried into the hall when she heard me at the front

* True to this day.

[  29  ]

door. She wanted to know where on earth I'd been, she was anxious about me. It had seemed unlikely an interview could last seven hours. I explained that the interview itself hadn't lasted more than an hour, but the work I'd been given to do had taken up the rest of the day. Mother opened her mouth and her eyes wide. There was a pause before she could speak.

"Work," she said finally, "you mean you have actually been given work to do by Marshall Field's?—and in those clothes?" she added under her breath, but I heard her.

I told her it might not mean a job, it was just an assignment. I found that word enjoyable to use. But I didn't want to talk about what had happened, I wanted it to be a surprise. I wanted my parents to be at the breakfast table, each reading a section of the *Tribune*, and to have whichever one of them was reading that section in which I appeared come upon my story. A Marshall Field advertisement just like the one every day that everyone read, except that this time it would not be like any of the other advertisements. It would be a story about Mary McCormick's costume written by Emily Kimbrough.

I savored this picture while I was dressing for dinner, and heard mother, in their bedroom next to mine, telling father about my day and protesting that I was being exasperating because I would give no details.

I was too tired and too bottled up with excitement to eat very much dinner; Gamin seemed tired, too. I went to bed early in order to be able, uninterrupted, to go over every minute of the day and also be able to be up and waiting when the newspaper arrived.

I got up at six o'clock the next morning and took Gamin with me to the Illinois Central Station a few blocks away, where I waited for the arrival of the early edition of the *Tribune*. I bought the first one off the pile as soon as the news agent had cut the string. But I didn't open it until I was back home and in my own room. It wasn't hard to find the Marshall Field advertisement, but a little more difficult to locate my story. I discovered it eventually under a sketch of Mary McCormick in the costume. The story read: "Mary McCormick, for her debut in the first presentation of the opera, *The Snowbird*, will wear this costume designed and executed by our Custom Apparel Section."

When mother and father some hours later read the *Tribune* at breakfast and exchanged sections across the table, I did not interrupt them with any mention of my story.

Later in my room, however, I said to myself, and was not only consoled but uplifted by the thought, "I am in print. Words I have written are printed today in the Chicago *Tribune*," because after all the line under the picture was the opening sentence of my three-page story.

Some time around noon I was told Miss Gardner wanted to speak to me on the telephone. I would have given almost anything in the world to send word I was out, but since it was mother who had answered the telephone and given me the message, this did not seem feasible. I sat at the instrument a little time before I said hello, hoping, as I said it, I would not bring up my breakfast.

They would like to have me start to work on Monday, Miss Gardner said, though between my nausea and the roaring in my ears I could not be sure I was hearing correctly. They needed a copywriter badly and liked the work I'd done on the McCormick story. I babbled something to the effect that indeed I could certainly be at work on Monday morning. Still giddy, but with my breakfast back in its proper tract, I ventured to mention that it had seemed to me they hadn't used a great deal of my story.

Her answer, in a very kind voice, was that it was not customary in a newspaper advertisement to run a three-page story, and that, furthermore, I'd turned in the story some time after the deadline. This was only the second time I had heard the word "deadline" and I did not grasp its meaning. Miss Gardner was continuing. She was particularly impressed, she said, by the expert typing.

So few girls who were not trained stenographers knew how to type at all. She and the head of the Bureau, to whom she had shown the piece, thought that with some training I could fit into the Field standard of writing.

I hung up without telling her that probably Miss Dennis, my father's secretary, was the person she wanted in the Advertising Bureau.

Mother came to the doorway in the living room and asked if that had been news about my job. "Yes," I told her, "that's what it was. I've got a job. I go to work on Monday."

Mother swooped down on me and flung her arms around my neck. Together we waltzed the length of the hall and back, while she did a kind of chant at the top of her lungs, "With your shield —I told you so—with your shield . . ."

It was Friday, and as always on that day, we went to the Chicago Symphony Concert at Orchestra Hall. While mother was dressing I slipped to the telephone again and called my father. I didn't feel like waltzing or chanting when I told him the whole true story, but he was amazingly cheerful. He said he could fix me up in no time. I asked bitterly if he intended having Miss Dennis go along to work with me.

He wanted to know if I hadn't mentioned something about spending the week end in Lake Forest with my friend, Eleanor Donnelley. I told him I was going and was taking a train after the concert. He would meet me, he said, at the gate, and I was to be on the lookout for him.

I found him without any difficulty. He was carrying a black case in his hand. "It's a portable typewriter," he explained, and handed it over to me. "I bought it for you. It's a present to celebrate your getting a job. Get to work on it, and every minute you have, write, 'Now is the time for all good men to come to the aid of their party.' I don't know why, but that's the sentence everybody learns on a typewriter. Miss Dennis says so. Keep at it."

I kept at it. Wherever Eleanor and I went that week end, the

Everywhere we went, I wrote, "Now is the time . . ."

typewriter went too, and everywhere we went I wrote, "Now is the time for all good men to come to the aid of their party."

On Monday morning at nine o'clock, I presented myself in a brown suit and without Gamin, at the counter of the Advertising Bureau of Marshall Field's on the ninth floor. My typewriter was in my hand, and my equipment as a copywriter of advertising was the ability to render six times in a minute, "Now is the time for all good men to come to the aid of their party."

# * 4 *

IN THE elevator, I had mused happily that coming to work
gave one a pleasanter approach to the Advertising Bureau than
applying for a job. Arriving at the counter, I nodded confidently
to the office boy, said a brisk "Good Morning," my hand on the
door to push it open as soon as he would click the button that
unlatched it.

"You're over there," the office boy said, pointing in the direction behind me and away from the Advertising Offices. "In there
with the stenographers. One of them can show you your desk.
Miss Gardner'll send for you as soon as she's ready to see you."

I had not anticipated an actual receiving line, but on the way
downtown I had conjured up a pleasant picture, people waving
from their desks, or coming to the door of the offices as I passed
on my way to Miss Gardner, and calling out, "So you're Miss
Kimbrough?"—"Delighted to have you with us," and maybe an
invitation or two for lunch.

I turned away from the door that did not click and went across
the aisle. A low railing set off a large open space, so filled with
desks there was barely room to move among them. Each desk,
it seemed to me, had an occupant, a young girl typing away on a
machine at a speed I had not as yet achieved with "Now is the
time . . ." The girl at the desk nearest the rail stopped typing and

smiled at me. I walked across the aisle to her. "I'm working in the Advertising Bureau," I said.

"That's right," she answered, "they told us you were coming over here. What's your name?"

"Emily Kimbrough."

She half turned in her chair, "Hi, girls," the typing stopped, "this is Emily Kimbrough. She's going to work in the Advertising Bureau. They haven't got office room for her over there, they sent word we were to give her a desk here. Emily, this is Mary, Josephine, Elsie—" She made the rounds. Each girl said hello as her name was called. "My name's Leona," she finished up the roll call. And I said, "Hello, Leona."

"Now then," she went on, "you all know each other. Where's that empty desk?" She turned back to me, "Gosh, we're so crowded in here you could have an empty desk for a week and not even notice it."

One of the girls called out, "This one, next to me." She held up her hand and indicated it.

"How do I get there," I asked, "walk across the tops?"

Some of the girls laughed, but quietly. Their voices were subdued.

Leona said, "I don't know as I would. It's the quickest way, but one of the bosses just might be coming out." She nodded her head across the aisle to the left of the Advertising Bureau. "Those are the Executive Offices over there; all the Big Boys, Mr. Simpson, Mr. Shedd, Mr. Yates, Mr. Corley—all of them."

I gasped. Those were the offices I had passed when I'd been looking for the Advertising Bureau. The young man I had seen at a desk in a sort of pen in front of those offices was there now. I lowered my voice although he couldn't possibly have heard us. I directed Leona's attention to him. "Which one is he?" I asked.

"He's not an executive," she told me. "He's just a kid. They're all old men. He's a special secretary and assistant to Mr. Simpson.

Mr. Simpson's the President. That boy's kind of an office boy, in a way, though higher up than that, if you know what I mean."

A girl at one of the back desks called out, "Now watch, Emily, I'll show you how to get to your desk. Go down two, then you can pass between that one and the next one, then go across three, and down one. You get it?"

It was like the maze at Hampton Court in which I'd got lost once the year before, but I didn't say so. I had to hold my typewriter with both hands above my waist as I made my way, because the space was too narrow for me to carry it at my side. The girls noticed the machine, and one of them asked why I'd brought it.

"Marshall Field's is no Santa Claus," she said, "but at least they provide you with a typewriter."

I'd reached my desk and I sat down at it. While I put my portable on the flat space in front of me and opened it, I was deciding whether or not to admit my stenographic shortcomings and the misconception of my ability that was the cause of my being hired. I decided in those close quarters I couldn't possibly keep it from them, so I blurted out the whole story.

The girls were wonderful. Not one of them by so much as a look indicated she resented my getting a job partly on a fluke. Instead they took it as a cute trick on Field's, and within a minute or two had worked out a system of helping me. They'd all keep a sort of watch, they agreed, and whenever anyone saw a member of the Advertising staff coming over, or one of the Big Boys passing by from the Executive Offices, she'd give me a signal. I was to whisk out the paper I would be pecking on, insert another, and rattle, "Now is the time for all good men . . ." until the coast was clear. Then I could pull that page out of the machine, put back the one on which I was working and go at my one-finger technique again.

The girls came over to my desk singly or in couples to examine my portable. It wasn't a good idea, they said, for everybody to

"Marshall Field's is no Santa Claus," she said, "but at least they
provide you with a typewriter."

gather around at once; it attracted attention. First thing you knew you had a notice from the timekeeper's office. You never could make out how they got to know these things, but they did.

"Once you're at Field's," the girls said, "they'll know everything about you. I don't know how, but they will. What you eat for breakfast, if you've got a fellow, and who he is. It's a good thing to remember. Just watch your step and take it easy, and you'll be all right."

Another one spoke up. "Anyway you're lucky," she said, "the Advertising Department rates special."

"Why?" I said.

"I don't know," she answered, "but it does. They get away with murder over there."

I had taken off my hat and coat and put them across one end of the desk. Elsie volunteered to show me the lockers where I could hang them, but I suggested I'd better wait to do that until after Miss Gardner had sent for me. She agreed that was a good idea, but added, "Did you punch the time clock?"

"Why, no," I told her. "I didn't know you were supposed to."

The girls near by who heard this gasped. The others had gone back to their typing. The ones who had heard me began to tell me all together something about having to punch the clock or I wouldn't get paid. The timekeeper's office had a fit if you forgot, and you just didn't get your pay, that was all.

In the midst of this, the office boy from the Advertising Bureau came across the aisle. I didn't see him until he stood at the rail and called my name. "Miss Gardner will see you now," he said.

I got up at once and, after two or three false tries, found a path again among the desks, and went over to the Bureau. He had already gone back to his desk. This time he clicked the latch and let me in.

Miss Gardner was at her desk. "I'm going to take you first," she said, "to introduce you to the other people in the department."

This was something of what I had anticipated on the way down that morning, but by the time it came I was preoccupied. "I didn't punch the time clock," I told her. "The girls say I have to do that immediately or I'll get into trouble. I'm awfully sorry. I seem to have made a bad start but I didn't know about the time clock."

"Never know about it," Miss Gardner said serenely. "They try to make us stick to a lot of rules here in the Bureau, but you can discourage them if you keep at it."

I asked her how you went about discouraging "them" and she explained.

"You might as well know right now," she said. "When you work in the Advertising Department, you don't keep regular hours that people in the rest of the store can observe. Sometimes there are photographs to be taken at night, sometimes a rush to get a thing out. Many times you have an assignment that will take you out of the store. So in my opinion it's ridiculous to classify us with the clock-punchers. I fixed that for myself by punching it every time I went past it. It took only a couple of weeks of that before the timekeeper's office sent a note requesting me to stay away from the instrument. I don't know what method you'll choose to use. You may find a better one.

"Now," she went on, getting to her feet, "I want you to meet the people in the Bureau. And one other thing," she said at the doorway of her office, "I don't like people to work for me who have clock-punching minds, turned on at eight-thirty and off at the stroke of half-past five. Come on. And then we'll go to the time-keeper's office and get you signed up."

We moved around the offices in the Bureau, starting with Mr. Schaeffer's, that was next door to Miss Gardner's. Mr. Schaeffer was the head of the department. His first name was Ray. Miss Gardner told me that before we went in, but she called him Mr. Schaeffer when she introduced me. He wore the widest, darkest, shell-rimmed glasses I had ever seen. He had a ruddy complexion, black hair and dark eyes behind the glasses. When he stood up to shake hands with me I discovered he was not six feet tall, but he gave the impression of size, probably because of his vitality. He was the heartiest man I had ever met. He took my hand as if it were a football and he were going to make a run with it. And his voice when he told me he was glad I was to be a member of the Advertising Family reverberated like a train announcer's in a railway station.

When we had left his office Miss Gardner told me he was known among the members of the Department as "Rog-Old-Scamp."

"Classmates of his from the University of Chicago are always calling him up. He invariably says, 'Well, Rog, Old Scamp, you son-of-a-gun, how've you been?' They can't all of them be named Roger, because I hear him tell Al Eddy in the next office when he's finished the conversation that so-and-so just called and the name isn't Roger. He needn't of course bother to repeat it to Al over the partition, everybody in the office has heard it, including Al. Mr. Schaeffer's one of the kindest men I ever knew," she added, "and he'll stand up to any and all of the executives for the people in this Bureau. His mind works slowly, you have to feed him an idea a spoonful at a time. But the funny thing is *he's* got ideas about Marshall Field & Company that are so big they can make your head spin."

While she was talking we had looked into the office next to Mr. Schaeffer's and had seen the man there talking on the telephone. She led the way back to her desk and I sat in the chair beside it, the same one I'd had the day of my first interview.

I asked her what kind of ideas Mr. Schaeffer had that were so big. I lowered my voice when I said this, because since the partitions went up only about six feet, and the doors to all the offices were open, I assumed we could be overheard. But Mr. Schaeffer was on the telephone.

Miss Gardner answered a little above her normal speaking voice. "He hammers at the conception," she explained, "of

Marshall Field's as a great institution. The greatest institution in the world. Not a retail department store and a wholesale store carrying merchandise to be advertised, but a vast organization dedicated to service. So he's always dinning at the newspaper people, 'Don't ever talk about the merchandise without talking about what's behind it—Marshall Field & Company.' "

She got up from her desk and started once more for the door and I followed her. She turned round to me, indicated Mr. Schaeffer still booming into the telephone and added, "To that man, Marshall Field & Company is food, drink, life, and very close to religion. I don't believe old Mr. Marshall Field himself could have loved the store or felt he owned it more completely than Ray Schaeffer feels this organization is his."

The man in the office next to Mr. Schaeffer's had finished his telephone conversation and Miss Gardner and I went in. His name was Mr. Eddy, Al Eddy. He was big too, but more plump than Mr. Schaeffer and far more easygoing in manner and speech. He had blue eyes, red hair and the fair complexion that goes with it. We didn't stay long in his office, and once we had moved on, I lost track of names. There were so many, and the people attached to them so busy, they had scarcely time to look up for a friendly hello and the assurance we'd be seeing each other.

Back in Miss Gardner's office again, she explained my location in the outer labyrinth and said she was sorry I couldn't be in the Bureau proper for the time being. "I've been running the newspaper advertising," she said, "but I'm taking over the magazine now. You've probably seen it. It's called *Fashions of the Hour*."

I said I had seen it. It came to the house.

"It goes to all the charge customers," she answered, "and it's given to anyone who asks for it. But it's never sent out unsolicited except to a charge customer. It has a circulation of about three hundred thousand. There are six issues a year. The January Number, that's principally for Linen sales and other special events. Then the Spring Number, that's the style number for all the Apparel Sections. The Summer Number features brides. Then it doesn't come out again until the end of August. That's the Go-Back-To-School Number, and it's almost entirely given over to the fourth floor, the young people's floor, as you probably know. October is what we call the Fall Exposition Number, the big style opening of the store with the Paris fashions, and after that the Christmas Number. I'm going to put you in here with me, rather than on the newspaper."

I was delighted to hear this and said so.

"All right," she went on, "let's get down to work. As soon as we settle in on this reorganization I hope to have a place in here for you, but for the time being you'll have to use the desk they gave you this morning."

I was so pleased to learn I was to work on the magazine, I wouldn't have cared if she'd told me I had to do my writing on top of one of the partitions. It also crossed my mind that before I became a little bit more proficient on the typewriter with sentences other than "Now is the time for all good men . . ." the farther out of earshot of the Advertising Bureau I remained, the longer I was likely to be a member of it. I urged her not to bother about finding a place for me, I would get along beautifully where I was.

I was sent back to my labyrinth carrying an armload of copies of *Fashions of the Hour,* and instructions to read them over paying particular attention to the back left-hand page of each issue. "Little Things Noticed on a Walk through the Store" was the title of this page. The body of it was made up of small boxed paragraphs each advertising an inexpensive bit of merchandise, ranging from a gadget out of the Household Utilities Section to a bottle of perfume.

Along with the magazines I carried a sheaf of requests from various sections recommending items in that section to be included in the coming issue. This was the page I was to write. "But," Miss Gardner had instructed, "you don't have to take those items requested. We're independent on the magazine. We take what we want, what we think is smart or unusual. The Buyers don't always like our selection but we have the last word; the management backs us up on the magazine. It's their baby and they certainly are indulgent parents."

I read all the issues I'd carried back to my desk and tried to put out of my mind Miss Gardner's assumption that, recently home from Paris, I would of course spot instantly the newest things in the store and those that had the Paris stamp of chic. I'd thought it inadvisable to tell her I had spent most of my time in Paris either sightseeing or attending classes at the Sorbonne, not so much from the high purpose of acquiring knowledge as from a low purse that prevented my doing much of anything else.

It was one o'clock by the time I'd finished reading the magazines. From half-past eleven on, the girls at the desks around me had been going off to lunch in groups. They didn't all go at the same time; I supposed that was so the whole place would not be deserted in case one of the executives whose work they did needed a stenographer. None of them asked me to go.

At one o'clock I put on my hat and coat, still across my desk, and went down to Charley's Door. I asked Charley if any of my friends were in that day for lunch, and he said he didn't think so, at least no one had left a message, so I went back up to the seventh floor and had lunch by myself in the Narcissus Room. When I got back I found a message on my desk that Miss Gardner wanted to see me. I was a little apprehensive lest she ask for my completed work and I hadn't as yet started it. But she only wanted to take me to the timekeeper, where I filled in a blank as an employee and was given a number on the time clock along with the stern injunction from the long, thin-nosed timekeeper to pay strict heed to punching regularly.

The timekeeper's office was on our floor along the aisle that led from the Advertising Bureau to the Household Utilities Department. As Miss Gardner and I walked back toward the Bureau, she stopped at a door opening off the aisle. "There's someone else I want you to meet," she said. "I forgot to bring you to him this morning. We generally do forget about Mr. Exley because he's off in this black cubbyhole, but just remember, not a word can go out of this office for print, that doesn't get Mr. Exley's OK."

Mr. Exley was sitting at a flat-top desk. There was a lamp burning on its top and that was the only light in the room. It was more like a closet than a room, with a doorway off the aisle and three solid walls that were partitions in the Advertising Bureau, as if this little and very poor space had been scooped out of the Bureau; and that was the way it had been made, I learned. Mr. Exley was bent over sheets of proofs set out on the desk in front of him. When Miss Gardner spoke his name he looked up at us, blinking. He wore gold-rimmed spectacles, was gentle, shy, but pleased to see us. Told I had joined the staff of the Advertising Department, he said he was happy to meet me and was sure I'd be happy working there. Miss Gardner told him I'd been studying in Paris. He blinked his eyes several times. "That's wonderful," he said, "that *is* wonderful. My goodness, you've been to Paris. Well, think of that."

When we left him, Miss Gardner walked with me to the railing that set off my maze of desks. We stood there while she told me about Mr. Exley. "He used to be a clerk in the basement," she said, "and there's a rule at Field's if any employee detects a misstatement or flaw of any sort in the Marshall Field advertising, he can bring the paper where this has appeared to the Advertising Bureau, point it out, and collect a dollar. Mr. Exley collected so many dollars, he was making more out of the flaws in the advertising than he was earning as a clerk. All of us in the Bureau hated him. No matter how many times we went over the advertising, day after day that little mild man would appear at the counter and say he'd brought up a few flaws he'd like to point out. We used to make all the excuses, that we worked under pressure and had to meet deadlines, we simply couldn't be expected not to have errors. But the management got to hearing about it—in Marshall Field's the management always gets to hear about everything—and the executives were riding Ray Schaeffer. So he had a brilliant idea of making Mr. Exley a member of the staff. There wasn't any room for him but somehow they dug out that little cubbyhole and put him in it. It couldn't be a worse place, dark as a pit with just that one lamp for somebody who does nothing but read print all day. But he's as happy as a bird, and we all love him. Not one word for print goes out of this department that doesn't go under his eye first, and there are no employees now collecting dollars for flaws."

"He seemed so touching," I said, "about my having been to Paris."

Miss Gardner agreed. "Do you know where he spends his vacations?" she asked and answered herself, "In the park. He told me so. He goes every day, takes a little package of sandwiches with him, sits on a bench, feeds the squirrels and watches children play. I'd be willing to bet he's never been on a train in his life. He struck up a friendship, through correspondence, with a professor at Oxford, if you can believe it; wrote to him about some point of English grammar he couldn't check to his satisfaction. He and the professor write to each other regularly now. Mr. Exley showed me some of the letters. He's as proud of them as a little boy over a baseball bat. And the professor has asked him to come to Oxford on a visit. It would be the greatest experience in his life, next to moving up here from the basement, but I don't suppose he'll ever get nearer to Oxford than Gary, Indiana."

As Miss Gardner started back to her office, she paused, "By the way," she said, "I don't believe I told you. When you go down through the store to get material for the page you're doing—and this is an important rule to remember—be sure to wear a hat."

I looked, I suppose, surprised, since I was.

"If you go without a hat you may be mistaken for a salesgirl."

"I don't mind one bit," I interrupted, to show that whatever I might be, I was certainly not a snob.

"I didn't suppose you did," she answered, "but Marshall Field & Company does mind. A customer might ask you to wait on her or give her some information. You would have to tell her you were not a member of that department. That, in the eyes of the management, would be embarrassing and annoying to a customer, and you would therefore be guilty of creating a dissatisfied customer. A dissatisfied customer is a catastrophe at Marshall Field's. Wear your hat, always, when you leave the office.

"But," she added, "take it off in the Bureau. There's no rule about that, but we discovered the Buyers get irritated when they come up to talk to us if they see us working with our hats on. They think we're putting on airs pretending we don't really work here. So we decided we wouldn't give them one more thing to be mad at us about."

This was the third time I'd heard about those Buyers; the first had been when the office boy had said the latch on the door was to keep them out. I wondered if the Advertising Bureau functioned as some sort of a complaint department. That would explain why the shoppers, or Buyers, as they seemed to call them, who came to the Bureau were always angry ones.

I asked Miss Gardner if this were so.

"Heavens!" she said, "you don't even know the beginnings of the department store vocabulary, do you? A Buyer is the head of a department. They're called Buyers because they buy the merchandise for the department to sell, and they do a lot of selling themselves, of course."

"Buyer" as a synonym for a head saleswoman had not occurred to me. In my limited-allowance shopping I had never ventured beyond the first saleslady who would notice me. But I had heard mother, in moments of indignation or urgency of some sort, ask to speak to the "head" of the particular department in which she was shopping.

Someone from the Bureau whom I had met in the morning, but whose name I didn't remember, came along the aisle and slipped her arm through Miss Gardner's. She smiled at me and they went on together to the Bureau.

At my desk I gathered up paper and pencil and put on my hat. Suddenly I felt as if I were back in Paris on my first day there, standing in front of my desk in the Pension. I could hear myself saying to Cornelia, "I'm writing down all the new words I've heard today. I'm going to do it every day and learn them while I'm brushing my hair. I thought I knew French, but I certainly don't."

On an impulse I sat down again at my desk and wrote on a piece of paper. "Put on hat in the store. Take off hat in the Bureau. Punch time clock, don't punch time clock. Buyer, head of department."

I wrote across the top of the page, "Marshall Field Vocabulary." Then I put the paper in the drawer of my desk, took a deep breath and set out on a walk through the store to notice little things and to meet Buyers.

# * 5 *

ON THE fourth floor Mrs. Hanley, Buyer for Children's Clothes, told me, and a number of shoppers near by, I was as welcome to her as diphtheria to a baby carriage. She urged me to get out of her section before she got really mad. "Those girls from the Advertising Bureau," she told the interested spectators, "they come in here when I'm busy with customers. They act like they're Mr. Simpson, or something."

The only thing I'd got out of that interview was the Buyer's name, Mrs. Hanley. I wrote it down. I'd intended to ask her if there were any special little things in her department she wanted me to notice, but I was swept out so fast I hadn't time even to look around for myself.

I'd chosen the fourth floor to start on only because a lot of people got off the elevator there, and I'd moved along with them. Mrs. Hanley's suggestion persuaded me the fourth was perhaps not a good starting place. I moved on down to the third. The Rest Rooms were on the third floor, large waiting rooms with plenty of comfortable chairs, the Wash Rooms behind. I sat down in one of the chairs and appraised the advantages and disadvantages of quitting my job then and there. The disadvantages weighed the heavier, I decided. To go home and tell mother I had given up my job at Field's was the equivalent of an interview with Mrs. Hanley, except that I could leave Mrs. Hanley.

I left the Rest Rooms and walked into the Book Department next door. I'd been in the Book Section a great many times as a customer, but I didn't know the names of any of the people who worked there. I remembered, however, a very pleasant young woman who was always at the Fiction Counter. She might, I hoped, pave my way to the Buyer. I found her without any difficulty. She was a little stocky, with dark hair, blue eyes, pink and white skin, dimples when she smiled and she always seemed to me on the verge of breaking into laughter.

"I don't know your name," I said to her, "but I've seen you lots of times when I've come in to buy books. I've got a job here now. I just started today. I'm in the Advertising Department. My name's Emily Kimbrough. Could I see the Buyer? I don't know what her name is."

The Fiction girl didn't laugh at this, instead she pulled in her dimples and looked warily toward the far end of the section. "Harriet Smith is my name," she said, "I've noticed you, too." She smiled briefly and then lowered her voice. "Mrs. Hahner is the name of the Buyer. You can see her, I guess, but I wouldn't advise it. The 'little boss' is on a rampage today. When her Irish dander is up, everybody better look out."

"What's the matter?" I asked and found I was very nearly whispering. Harriet Smith's uneasiness was catching.

"The management's tried to put some new regulation on the section without consulting her. At least that's the news on the moccasin telegraph." I found out later that in Marshall Field vocabulary "moccasin telegraph" equals "grapevine."

"Is a Buyer always consulted?" I asked.

"Even the top ones up on the ninth floor consult my boss," Harriet assured me, "or at least tell her what they're going to do. No, they don't do it for all the Buyers, but my boss is different.

[ 52 ]

Mrs. Hanley, Buyer for Children's Clothes, told me, and a number of
shoppers near by, I was as welcome to her as diphtheria
to a baby carriage.

Everybody steps around Marcella Hahner. You'll see. But just take my advice, don't see her today."

I thanked my new friend, Harriet Smith, and eased out of the Book Department. Rugs were next door, but scarcely under the category of "*little* things noticed." I stopped in the candy section beyond.

The floorwalker I asked to direct me to the head of the department turned out to be the head of the department. His name was Mr. Cavenaugh. No good, I decided on the instant, could come of an interview that began by my mistaking the head of a department for a floorwalker, and I edged away from him, sideways, like a land crab, my eyes on the nearest exit. Mr. Cavenaugh walked along beside me, asking pleasantly what he could do for me, and so presently I stopped edging and told him I was there for the purpose of noticing things, and writing about them in *Fashions of the Hour*. I was not very coherent, my first face-to-face encounter with a Buyer addled me. But Mr. Cavenaugh was soothing. He seemed even glad to see me. It occurred to me that if candy did this to Mr. Cavenaugh, books soured Mrs. Hahner, and children's clothes embittered Mrs. Hanley, you ought to consider very carefully where you were going to work at Field's.

By way of broaching this general topic as a way of getting better acquainted, I asked Mr. Cavenaugh how long he had been in the Candy Section. "Twenty years," Mr. Cavenaugh said proudly, "before that I was a floorwalker." He was leaning against the counter. As he said this he straightened up, looked in the mirror behind the counter, motioning a salesgirl standing there to move a little to one side, and adjusted his tie. "You never get over floorwalker training," he declared. "Neatness is one of the first requisites. I think that shows in my department here."

I assured him everything in it glistened.

"That's what I tell my girls," he confided. "Make it shine, I say."

"Were you a floorwalker here?" I prodded him for the story, feeling we were getting better acquainted every minute.

"There wasn't any Candy Section then," he answered, "but every time Mr. Shedd came through my department, I'd say to him, 'Mr. Shedd, we ought to have a Candy Section in the store.' Or again I'd say, 'Mr. Shedd, I think it's terrible Marshall Field & Company hasn't got a Candy Section.' So one day he said to me, 'Well, Cavenaugh, all right, go ahead and start one.' That's all there was to it. They set me up a section and I've been running it ever since."

I said I hadn't any idea you could make suggestions to the heads of the Company. Mr. Cavenaugh pounded his fist on a counter to emphasize his statement that *anybody* could get to the top people up on the ninth floor. A packing boy in the basement, if he had an idea, could go right up to Mr. Simpson with it. And Mr. Simpson would listen. And every Buyer was told to listen to the ideas people in his department might have—and try them out if they seemed good.

We never got around to noticing things in the Candy Department. Mr. Cavenaugh said for me not to bother. He'd send up a list of nice items he was sure *Fashions of the Hour* readers would like.

The second floor looked crowded, so I moved on down to the first, with a plan of working my way back up to the ninth.

The Stationery Department was immediately in front of the elevator I used and didn't seem crowded. An elderly lady with white hair and a kind face stood behind one of the counters. I asked her if I could see the head of the department.

"Now?" she asked, adding in the same breath, "No, I don't think so."

"I'm from the Advertising Department," I explained and hoped to tell her I was doing a page for *Fashions of the Hour*. This was something I enjoyed telling, but I was interrupted.

"I can't get used to you girls in the Advertising Department.

I've been at Marshall Field's for thirty years. Bredin is my name, Ellen Jane Bredin. I've seen a lot of changes in the store, but you girls sashaying around the store with your papers and pencils and your notebooks as pert as you please is enough to make Mr. Field turn in his grave."

I could have assured her I didn't feel pert. To date there had been nothing about working for Field's to give me that feeling. My impression was, however, that she was not interested in how I felt, but might be a little more kindly disposed if I asked about her.

"Have you always worked here in the Stationery Department?" I chose this question as a good beginning. It was not.

She flared up indignantly. "I do not work in the Stationery Department. I'm in charge of the engraving."

The responsibility of that job, I assured her quickly, must be terrific. She was somewhat mollified. "I was an apprentice for five years before I was allowed even to take an engraving order," she announced proudly.

I asked if there were a lot of orders then for engraving.

She regarded me witheringly. "Ten, twenty times more than now. When printing came in—nasty, cheap stuff—it just about cleaned out the engraving business. Why, in the old days," she was interested now and leaned across the counter toward me, "women would order five hundred cards at a time. The society women on the South Side were always at home on Mondays and they had cards for it; the West Side ladies had Tuesdays, and the North Side, Wednesdays. They were real ladies in those days. They didn't even carry their own dies when they came in. A butler came with them. He'd walk about five feet behind, carrying the die." She broke off suddenly. "Here comes our Buyer now," she said, "but you better not speak to him."

A little, round man was coming down the aisle toward us almost at a jog trot. Abreast of him a tall, slim young man, carrying a leather portfolio under one arm, was easily keeping up in long,

[ 57 ]

unhurried steps. By the time they reached us, the little man had taken out of his vest pocket a large gold watch three times, looked at it, and slipped it in again, shaking his head anxiously as if each reading were a worrying surprise. He reminded me instantly of the White Rabbit in *Alice*.

As they reached us, Miss Bredin said to the little man, "Here's a young lady from the Advertising Bureau. She wants to see you."

"Can't possibly see her. Not possibly," the little man said. He took out his watch for the fourth time, looked at it, shook his head, pursed his lips and added, "I ought to be on the ninth floor right now. Simpson sent for me. Can't imagine what for. Mustn't keep him waiting.

"How've we done on that Crane cream vellum, gilt-edged, Lot 2498? That's the number, isn't it?" He turned to the young man.

The young man nodded. "That's right," he said.

Miss Bredin spoke as soothingly as a nurse to a fractious child. "I put the records on your desk on the left-hand side. I knew Ed was coming in today. How are you, Ed?" she said to the young man.

"Fine as silk," he told her and winked at her over the top of his companion's head. "I'll see you before I go."

She nodded understandingly.

Miss Bredin's boss turned and trotted off again in the direction from which he had come, the young man strolling a little behind him.

Miss Bredin sighed. "The boss's a worrier," she said. "Ed—he represents Crane papers—will come back here and we'll make up the order between us and the boss will sign it. He's a smart merchandiser, though," she added proudly.

Friendship with Miss Bredin was the way to the boss. I made up my mind to this as I watched the two men disappear down the side aisle in the direction, I supposed, of the Buyer's office. I turned back to Miss Bredin and urged her, if she weren't busy, to tell me more about how it was at Field's when she had come into the department. She, in turn, was pleased at my asking, but would have to leave off, she said, if any customer came along.

"Well," she began, "one of the big differences," and nodded her head in the direction the little man and Ed had taken, "is right there. He's a nervous man, I grant you, but all Buyers are nervous nowadays. It's the system. Why, in those early days, sometimes we'd keep articles for six years, if necessary. We knew our merchandise was good and we'd sell it off eventually. Nowadays, they high-pressure you, so if you have your stock for six months it's a crime. Buyers could take it easier then. Now, when you have to sell or close out your stuff in six months, it's no wonder they get gray-headed and take to smoking, or worse. They're just run ragged from upstairs."

I asked if the other people, the clerks, worked harder now than they did then.

She said they worked harder now but longer then. In the old days they'd begun at eight in the morning and often worked through until midnight, taking inventory or making up orders. On nights when they worked late they got supper money of fifty cents. Now there were all kinds of rules about how late and how many hours you were allowed to work. In Miss Bredin's opinion this was a lot of nonsense. Hard work never hurt anybody. And nobody ever got ahead without it.

One difference she repeated several times, tapping her finger on the counter to emphasize it: "In those days we didn't have sales talk, not that high-powered stuff that's come in now. I was taught to serve, not push. I'd say to a customer that couldn't make up her mind about something, 'See if you need it when you get home, and then come back tomorrow.' I never tried to persuade her she did need it. Of course we always used to cater to palatial people. Now we say, 'Come on in, all of you.'"

Salesgirls wore, she said, black dresses with high collars, and were not allowed to put on jewelry. An overseer made the rounds continuously to see how the clerks were dressed. "We weren't supposed to dress as well as customers. We were to be neat but not competitive. We must be always self-effacing. That's what they were always saying to us. But the men clerks could wear whatever they wanted."

I asked her if she thought the salespeople were more democratic now along with the customers. Her opinion was, she said, clerks were getting more stylish and customers getting commoner. She marked the beginning of the change in clerks when they were told to say to a customer, "May I help you?" instead of "Have you been waited upon?" Saying "waited upon" kept clerks in the servant class; "helping" somebody made them feel more important.

She described an annual outing in the days when Mr. Selfridge was General Manager. All the clerks were taken to his place in the country, she said. Mrs. Selfridge would lead the children by the hand down to where they all stood, so that everybody could see her and the little ones. "Just like royalty," Miss Bredin called it.

"In those days," she continued, "there were a lot more men clerks than women. In the Jewelry Section, for instance, women weren't allowed. In Perfume, they had both men and women, but Field's was the first store women would work in, because it was considered the most respectable place."

I asked if they ever had any colored clerks. "No," she said emphatically. "They never have had." I smiled a little to myself at this positive assertion, because I happened to know from a colored cook of ours that there were working at that moment at Field's a considerable number of colored clerks, both men and women, "Except," our cook had said, "nobody at Field's knows it, and we don't tell on 'em. They've passed."

I didn't reveal this small bit of knowledge of mine to Miss Bredin. But the idea reminded her of something else to tell me. "We get a lot of colored customers," she said, "nowadays. And I always treat them like everybody else. As a matter of fact," and she chuckled, "the whole idea of paper napkins came from a colored customer. And it's one of our biggest selling items."

She went on to explain—and I treasured every word to take back to our cook—that a Mrs. Edward Morris, the wife of an important Negro lawyer in Chicago, had been buying something from Miss Bredin one day and mentioned they had a summer place at St. Joe, Michigan, where they entertained a great many guests all summer. They also had a peach orchard and grew fine peaches. Their guests were particularly partial to peaches, and it disturbed Mrs. Morris, she said, to see peach stains on her nice linen. She wondered why it wouldn't be possible to have napkins made of paper. Miss Bredin saw no reason why it wouldn't be possible, thought over the idea, and the next thing anybody knew, there were paper napkins in the Stationery Department selling, in Miss Bredin's words, "like hotcakes."

"Items like those," she pointed out, "move a lot faster nowadays than handsome monogrammed stationery. Girls going to boarding school, for instance, used always to be furnished with a writing portfolio and beautiful monogrammed paper to go with it. It was considered part of their standard equipment. Now they don't bother about such things but get any old kind of printed stationery and keep it in the box it was sold in, as far as I can see."

Birth announcements was another item that had fallen off, she volunteered. They used to be set up elegantly, and she described them. "In those days," she insisted, "everybody bought pink-edged for a boy, blue for a girl. Pink came from the color worn by a Cardinal, and blue was associated with the Madonna." She attributed the changes to the publication of Eugene Field's poem, "Little Boy Blue." Everybody was crazy about that poem, and the public took up blue for boys.

A voice called down the aisle, "Bredin, Bredin."

I turned around. Her boss was having at us on the double, waving a sheaf of papers in one hand. "Beat it," said Miss Bredin.

I did not visit any other section of the first floor on the Wabash side, as that section of the store is called, feeling that Miss Bredin's boss, on the run, might turn up anywhere. I crossed the covered alleyway that separates, on the first floor, the two halves of the store, and went into the State Street division. The Notion Counter there was jammed with customers. I skirted round it and came to the Perfume Section.

Mr. Tracy was the Perfume Buyer. A glittering blonde lady behind the counter told me his name. "Mr. Tracy's our Buyer," she said, "that's him right now down at the end of this counter." She lifted a hand and the nails sparkled as she pointed toward a tall man with broad shoulders, narrow face, who was standing at the far end of the aisle from me, looking over his domain, his arms folded across his chest.

He was happy to make my acquaintance, he said, and what could he do for me? Except for Mr. Cavenaugh's, this was the only welcome I had received and I responded to it with an enthusiasm that bordered on hysteria, babbling that anything he would like me to notice from his department I'd be more than glad to write up for a page in *Fashions of the Hour*. He assured me this would certainly be a fine thing to do and he had just the item *Fashions of the Hour* readers would respond to. If I'd care to step with him to his office he'd give himself the pleasure of showing it to me.

By this time we were almost bowing to each other, and we pranced together to a tiny office screened off in a corner behind one of the counters. There were at least fifteen or twenty brands of perfume, each in a fancy bottle, on his desk. He selected one and handed it to me. "That's our very own," he said, "Blue Rose. It's a Marshall Field product. We make it ourselves. Finest perfume produced today." He gave me the price on each size bottle in which it could be purchased and I wrote it all down. Out of the top drawer of his desk he drew a small leaflet. Holding it in one hand and tapping it with the forefinger of his other to emphasize the importance of the document, he said, "This is a wonderful writeup of the product. All you have to do is take the words right out and you'll have everything you want."

My idea had been to use my own words but I took the paper and thanked him.

"Here," he said and pushed the bottle toward me, "take this along too, and keep it. I'd like you to try it for yourself. See how you like it. You'll never use another perfume after you've once applied this. Wait a minute," he added, "I'll give you something to go with it." He got up from the desk and hurried out of the office.

I hadn't thanked him for the perfume nor even taken it in my hand because I was not sure I ought to accept it. This might be bribery, I thought, the kind of thing you read about in the papers. But I also conjectured, while I awaited Mr. Tracy's return, a possibility of doing an item for *Fashions of the Hour* on the Fur Section and having an ermine coat pressed around my shoulders by a grateful Buyer.

Mr. Tracy returned carrying a long cut-glass perfume bottle with an atomizer top. "Put your perfume in this," he suggested, "and then spray it on you. You can cover a bigger area than with just drops behind your ears. It gives off an all-over aroma that way."

I had never owned an atomizer. The only times I'd ever even seen one used were at the movies when vamps, like Theda Bara, went around spraying a room in a scent anticipating the arrival of a young man who was to be enslaved. The prospect of using this on a young man I knew named Edward Kratz was enough to make me more than willing to risk disgrace from bribery. I thanked Mr. Tracy heartily, took the perfume complete with atomizer, and left.

On my way out of the department I passed the blonde saleslady who'd directed me to Mr. Tracy. She saw me and pointed to my bottles. "See you got a present," she called out.

Since she had spotted instantly Mr. Tracy's offering, it occurred to me that to visit other Buyers carrying this loot might be con-strued as a hint. It would be discreet, I decided, to put it in my desk drawer with my Vocabulary List.

Returning to the ninth floor, I found on my desk a note that read, "If you get back by four-thirty, come to tea on the seventh floor. I'm the small blonde." The note was signed, "Buff Corse." I remembered her instantly among the people I'd met that morning in the Bureau, because she was so small and so blonde, with curly hair fluffed out at the sides and gathered on top of her head in soft rather misty disorder. Under this tam o'shanter her face had looked as tiny as a child's, but her eyes were very large and very blue. I'd been charmed, too, by the rouge she wore, baby-pink, and pressed in a perfect circle on each cheek, the way dolls' cheeks were painted.

I went to the seventh floor and without any difficulty found Buff Corse at a table by a window, her hair silhouetted against it. Within five minutes after I had sat down I realized she was from the South and more amusing than anyone I had met in a long time.

I told her how nice it was of her to ask me. She apologized for not having been more attentive in the morning but said they'd been racing toward that old deadline, and she hadn't been able to say more than a curt "howdy." She'd had it in her mind later to ask me to lunch but had discovered she didn't have enough money and someone else had the dollar. That really wouldn't have bothered her, she assured me, but by the time she'd found out about the dollar and was going to ask me to pay for my lunch and maybe hers, depending on how much she ate, I was gone from my desk and she couldn't find me.

I was sorry, I told her, she hadn't found me because I'd felt a little dreary at lunch. I'd hoped maybe one of the girls around me would ask me, but no one had suggested it.

Buff shook her head ruefully. "Never in this world," she said, "at least never in this store. We're the worst bunch of snobs you ever saw. A salesgirl wouldn't be seen with a stockgirl, and a stenographer wouldn't eat lunch with a salesgirl. A salesgirl is socially above an elevator operator and a Buyer is above everybody except the executives."

I asked where we came in.

"I don't think we've been really catalogued yet," Buff told me after considering this for a minute, "but I know a stenographer would think we were much too high-falutin' to step out with her class. The Buyers, I know, would like to put us in the social division of poor white trash, but they don't quite dare, because we have dealings with the ninth-floor executives, like Cabots speaking to God. So though they fight us, they do a lot of scraping to us at the same time. All except Marcella Hahner. She wouldn't bow nor scrape to anybody."

I said I'd heard something of that when I'd gone down to her department earlier in the afternoon.

Buff's eyebrows rose. "Baby!" she said and closed her eyes. "What you walked into. I'm surprised you got out with your skin on."

"Mrs. Hahner wasn't around," I explained.

"You don't have to tell me that," Buff interrupted. "Next time you send an advance notice. Ask for an appointment, make your manners and humble yourself, girl."

I shivered at what I had escaped and changed the subject as soon as Buff had ordered tea and a special cinnamon toast. "The most succulent," she promised, "you've ever tasted."

I asked about the dollar she'd gone to find before asking me to lunch.

"A very important feature of the Advertising Bureau," she insisted. Where it had sprung from originally, no one knew, but it was a dollar available to anyone short of funds. Whenever you took it you marked the fact on a chart, and then anyone in need of it could apply to the person who'd had it last. But it could only go out to one person a day. "So," Buff said, "when I got to it I was too late. It had already gone. You can't apply for it a day ahead, but it's only fair to tell you now that on the day before payday, you want to get in mighty early with your application."

Unexpectedly she waved. "Here comes Helen," she said, "Helen Thompson."

A girl came up to our table from behind me. She was blonde too, a little plump. She looked as if she laughed easily and would be fun to know. I remembered her. She was a little out of breath as she sat down between us.

"I didn't know whether you could get here or not, so I didn't order for you," Buff told her.

"That's all right," Helen answered, "I didn't think I really could make it."

Buff leaned across to me. "The Bureau is taking up a collection to buy Helen a scooter. If you'd care to sign up we'd be glad to include you. She covers the store and she takes it on the gallop."

Helen chuckled. Her laugh was deep and contagious. I knew I was going to like her. I already liked Buff. This was turning out to be a good first day, I thought, what with Mr. Tracy's perfume and Miss Bredin and Mr. Cavenaugh, leaving out Mrs. Hanley and counting all to the good my escaping Mrs. Hahner.

I asked Helen if she worked on the newspaper too.

"No," she said, "I do promotional work."

I groaned. "Nobody can say three sentences around here," I explained, "without giving me a word or a phrase I've never heard of in my life."

The other two agreed it had been like that for them in the beginning. But after a while you forgot other people didn't know the talk of the store.

Helen explained that promotional work had to do with special events, getting them organized, setting them up, and then doing publicity on them. It might be decorated rooms for the Furniture Department, or tables set in an unusual way to go along with the Linen sales. "I work a lot with Frances Hooper," Helen added.

"She runs all the advertising and promotional work for the fourth floor, that's the Children's and Young People's Department."

"I know," I interrupted, "I went there today and got chased out."

Helen said she wasn't surprised. "Hanley's a nervous woman to start with," she said. "And Hooper's ideas are, to say the least, original. She has one about every hour. Hooper's a genius, but she's got Hanley so agitated, all you have to say to the woman is 'Advertising Bureau' and she begins to twitch all over. We're going to have monkeys there next week," Helen added ruminatingly.

Our tea and cinnamon toast arrived. Helen told the waitress she'd have a chocolate sundae and another order of cinnamon toast. When this had been taken care of I said I'd be obliged if someone would tell me what was meant by "monkeys."

Helen was eating a piece of my cinnamon toast and very nearly choked on it. "That's no advertising nor store term," she gasped, "I mean monkeys, live monkeys. We're going to have them in the Children's Department. It's an idea of Hooper's. Hanley's climbing things herself already."

I asked what the monkeys were going to do. Helen wished she knew, she said. So did everybody else. Only Hooper's answer was it didn't make any difference. Children always loved to come to see monkeys, so if you put monkeys in the Children's Department they'd come with their mothers to see them and the mothers would buy them clothes. It was a logical sequence.

Buff turned the conversation politely to me and asked how my first day had gone. I told them, trying to say it modestly, in my opinion it had gone very well. I'd been told to do a page on "Little Things Noticed on a Walk through the Store" and Mr. Cavenaugh and Miss Bredin had been so nice they'd practically taken things right over for me. Mr. Tracy had gone even further. I admitted the bit of loot and asked if they thought it was all right for me to take it.

Buff put her head in her hands and groaned. Helen laughed, and then apologized for it. Her sundae and cinnamon toast came along and she applied herself to eating. She had gone through my order but went on to her own with relish.

Buff picked up the conversation with an explanation of their behavior at the recital of my little triumphs. "Emily," she began, "you have been taken for a buggy ride. Beginning with Mr. Cavenaugh. Mr. Cavenaugh is a smooth gent. Probably learned it from being a floorwalker. He doesn't want you picking up items to advertise. He wants to push, through *Fashions of the Hour*, some little numbers he's got himself involved in that aren't going too well, and recoup on his mistake—or maybe plug a steady, sure-selling item he's bound to do big volume with. He doesn't want to be bothered with some chic little novelty you might spot. He'd have to put in a big order for it in case *Fashions of the Hour* readers took to it, and maybe they wouldn't. So he has a little risk. This way he has no risk and no trouble. . . ."

"And no news value," Helen put in and went back to her cinnamon toast.

"Now we come to Miss Bredin," Buff continued. "I myself would not be surprised if across Miss Bredin's heart were writ in fine engraving, 'Miss Bredin requests the pleasure' or perhaps 'Miss Ellen Jane Bredin at home on Tuesdays'—"

"Let's not be coarse," Helen threw in.

Buff ignored her. "Miss Bredin," she went on, "will present to her boss a little paragraph for *Fashions of the Hour* written with the sprightliness of an obituary notice on the necessity for every lady of refinement to own calling cards, etcetera, engraved at Marshall Field's. Her boss will send this on gratefully and that will be your news note in *Fashions of the Hour* from the Stationery Department."

"Well," I put in hopefully, "I did get a lot of information about the store and the way it was in the old days. That might come in handy some time."

Helen interrupted me. "Anybody who's been here ten years or more wants to talk about the old days. The store affects them that way. Lord, they'll grab anybody who'll listen. Ancient Mariners, all of them."

She would have elaborated on this but Buff put up her hand. "Wait," she said, "we now come to Mr. Tracy. The noblest of them all. Helen, I'll bet you the Bureau dollar that what Mr. Tracy pressed into our little friend's reluctant hand was a bottle of Blue Rose perfume."

"It was," I said.

My friends nodded at each other.

"Blue Rose," continued Buff, "brewed from a witch's caldron."

"Why is Mr. Tracy so crazy about it?" I managed to ask.

"Because," Helen took it up, "it is a Marshall Field product, made by our own hands, sent out into the world by Marshall Field & Company wholesale. And since wholesale is the power behind the retail, it can push its product on the Buyer. And when Mr. Tracy feels the hot breath of wholesale on the back of his neck, he in turn pushes Blue Rose, by fair means or foul, at the Advertising Bureau. But we aren't taking any. Our slogan is 'Blue Rose only once in a blue moon.'"

"That's really the trouble," Buff reflected. "It's the name. We've tried and tried in the Bureau to make them change it. Blue Rose is an unattractive idea. There isn't any such thing. Nobody wants to see such a thing. So why would you want to smell it? But you can't buck the wholesale."

Helen added one more note of consolation to me. "If you come into the Bureau," she warned, "sprayed with Blue Rose, you'll be hung out of the window to air."

We'd finished our tea; more explicitly Helen had finished some of our food and all of hers. We left the tearoom, stopping at the desk on the way out to pay, Buff observing she hoped I didn't interpret her invitation to tea as an indication she was going to pay for mine. As we got out of the elevator on the ninth floor and started toward the Bureau, Helen asked Buff how she'd signed out.

"Just 'off the floor,'" Buff said. "What did you say today?"

"Section Twenty-one. Bunker's a good scout, he'll always cover up for you. Say you've just left, or something."

Buff turned to me. "Don't worry if you put down tearoom. It's all right every once in a while. It's just not a good thing to overdo it."

I answered that I felt like Mrs. Hanley, beginning to twitch, because I hadn't the faintest idea what they were talking about. We'd reached the gate to my labyrinth and my desk and we stopped there. For a minute neither of them spoke.

It was Helen who finally said in a hushed voice, the one inviolable rule of the Advertising Bureau was, always sign where you could be found on the chart bearing your name and hanging beside the door. This was primarily for the newspaper people in case a sudden crisis occurred, but everybody in the Bureau observed the rule. Not to sign out was about the only thing that could really get you into trouble.

"I see," I said.

Buff patted my arm as I pushed open the gate. "If I were you," she advised, "taking one thing with another, I'd just cross this day off the calendar. Make like it never came up. Start all over again tomorrow."

## * 6 *

THE FOLLOWING day I walked through the store getting
material for the "Little Things Noticed" page. I wrote down the
price of each item I selected and the name of the section from
which it had come. From an employee's manual sent to my desk
by the timekeeper's office I learned the area I had to cover was
sixty-three and a half acres. I did not encounter a Buyer in any
of them, and I counted this an achievement in artful dodging.
I counted a further achievement a meticulous observance of the
signing-out rule I'd learned from Buff and Helen.

Each time I moved from one section to the next on my trip,
I telephoned the office boy in the Bureau and told him my destination. I worked out this scheme as an efficient time-saver to
show my employers that I was using my head rather than my
feet, instead of returning each time to sign for myself the
place of my next visit. But after the fifth or sixth call, the office
boy asked me to hold the line a minute.

Miss Gardner came on the telephone. "Miss Kimbrough," she
said, and her voice sounded a little harassed, "please don't keep
telephoning Albert your exact whereabouts. He has other things
to do than note your progress through the store. It's very consci-
entious of you, but signing on the chart, 'covering the store' or
simply 'off the floor' will be quite sufficient."

After I had apologized and hung up, I made a note to put on my Vocabulary List the phrases, "off the floor" and "on the floor," with the explanation they were not to be taken literally. The first time a clerk seeing me write down information about an item I was noticing had asked me if I wanted to see the Buyer, adding she was on the floor, I had been startled. I discovered it meant only she was not away from her department.

At noon I broke my journey by stopping for lunch, returning first to my ninth-floor base in order to leave my writing paraphernalia and gather up my coat, pocketbook and gloves. I was wearing my hat. I found on my desk a note from Buff, inviting me to join her for lunch. "It's early in the week for it," I read, "but let's meet at the Domestic Science Tearoom," and the address followed, Tower Building, Madison Street and Michigan Avenue. There was no time mentioned but I went across the aisle and looked at the chart. She had signed out for lunch. I signed myself out, thinking as I wrote that I was getting the hang of the chart after all, learning to read as well as write on it.

There were two girls at the table with Buff in the Domestic Science Tearoom. She introduced them, Margaret Haggett and Eleanor Hunter, both from the Advertising Bureau. "You met them yesterday," Buff added, "but you probably don't remember."

I said I did remember meeting them but I still hadn't got names straightened out.

Margaret was small and blonde, Eleanor taller and with reddish hair. Both of them were more formal than Buff and Helen had been, though Margaret told me to call her Peg.

I asked Helen's whereabouts and Buff shuddered. "My friends," she pronounced solemnly, "there is a 'tohubohu' of cosmic proportions going on at this moment between the ninth and the fourth floors, and our Helen is in the middle of it."

"My Lord," she interrupted herself, "here she comes. I thought maybe she was dead by now."

Helen came down the room making her way among the

[ 72 ]

crowded tables at a curious gait like a beginner on roller skates. She let herself gingerly down into a chair. "Hello," she said, "my feet hurt so they feel as though they might come off."

"Hooper been jumping on them?" Buff inquired sympathetically.

Helen shook her head. "I've been running," she said, "since eight-thirty this morning."

One of the other girls murmured there was no news in that. But Helen was not diverted.

"It's those damn monkeys," she explained. "Hooper and I only realized this morning that monkeys aren't housebroken. Wouldn't you think as smart as monkeys are you could train them in that direction? Well, you can't. The Toy Department brought it to our attention with the announcement that not at any price were they going to have monkeys. They argued they weren't going to take a loss on damaged merchandise no matter how much they sold. It seemed a reasonable argument to me, but you can't down Hooper. Not for long. In two minutes she came up with another idea. It may surprise you," she paused dramatically.

We urged her on.

"Stork pants," she said, "stork pants on the monkeys and move them over to the Infants' Wear Section. You ought to have heard the Buyer over there when that news was brought to her. And guess who was commissioned to bring it?"

"I heard Hooper on the telephone," Buff interrupted. "I guess it was the Infants' Wear Buyer she was talking to."

"She had it easy," was Helen's comment. "I was *with* the Buyer. I'm surprised you didn't hear her without benefit of telephone announcing what she thought of monkeys in her section advertising stork pants. She wasn't very coherent, but I gather that, among other things, stork pants was one item she never needed to advertise anyway. Her only trouble was keeping in a big enough supply. She certainly didn't need apes climbing around showing them off."

I ventured to ask how Helen thought it would all turn out. "That's anybody's guess," Helen said wearily, "only I'm betting on Hooper. The whole fourth floor is on the rampage now. Every other Buyer there is afraid the monkeys will be moved on to him. They're storming up to the ninth floor, Hooper won't see them. They're threatening to go all the way to Mr. Simpson. I've been trying to soothe them, relaying messages from Hooper, hurrying back to her with messages I modify on the way; I wouldn't dare repeat them verbatim. Now she's given me another job that's a honey. Oh, well, it will get me out of the store anyway."

She pointed to a package she held on her lap. "Stork pants, dears," she said. "I'm on my way to the monkeys to try them on for size. What's for lunch? How do we happen to be here on a Tuesday?"

The others explained to me that lunch at the Domestic Science Tearoom cost only forty cents. It was run in conjunction with a big Domestic Science school and served only one dish, whatever had been cooked that morning, together with hot homemade rolls and butter, and tea, coffee or milk, ice cream for dessert. The girls in the Bureau usually saved the place for around the end of the week when funds were low, but Buff had thought it a good place for me to know about as early as possible. Anybody would know the more expensive places.

I appreciated this and told them so. The lunch was delicious. We left Helen at the door, the rest of us went back to the store. On our way to the elevator I said I was only going to the ninth floor to pick up my notebook and pencil. I still had a considerable number of sections to cover for my "Little Things Noticed," but I already had such a case of museum legs from the morning's tramp, I didn't know how I was going to hold out.

The girls were sympathetic and volunteered to take my coat, bag and gloves for me. Margaret Haggett had a notebook and pencil she lent me. This would save a little traveling, she said, and I was grateful.

I got off at the fifth floor, which was as far as I had progressed during the morning; they went on. In the Drapery Department I was looking at some Toile de Jouy prints in drapery fabrics, wondering if I could include them as "Little Things Noticed," when a woman spoke to me. "Are you an employee?" she asked. I jumped, a little startled. I'd not heard her come up beside me.

"Yes," I said, "I am." Then suddenly remembering I must not dissatisfy a customer, I added hastily, "but I'm not in this section." I tried to keep from sounding superior. "I'm from the Advertising Bureau."

"Wherever you're from," the woman answered, "you're not dressed according to store regulations. Black or navy blue are the only colors permitted, as you should know very well. Black shoes and black stockings. What you're doing in a brown outfit with brown shoes and hose, I can't imagine except you people in the Advertising Bureau seem to think the rules don't include you. They do, though, and I'm going to have to report this."

"I'm new here," I said weakly. "I haven't learned all the rules. There seem to be a lot of them. I didn't know about clothes."

"I don't call that any kind of an excuse," was her answer. "When you come to work at Marshall Field's, it's your business to find out what's expected of you." She stalked off.

A clerk had been standing on the other side of the counter while I was being reprimanded, but in my embarrassment I had not looked at her. She spoke up. "They've always got it in for you Advertising girls," she said. "The nerve of those overseers. They act as if they own the place."

I muttered something about this being only my second day in the store.

"Sure," she agreed, "you can't be expected to know everything. But they're awfully strict about dress regulations. Why, they fired a friend of mine last year because she bobbed her hair. She was at the Information Desk on the third floor."

"They didn't," I gasped.

She nodded. "They certainly did. But," she added triumphantly, "they had to take her back. There was an awful row about it. It even got into the papers. I'm surprised you didn't see it. And, by golly, Field's had to give in. But the rule is now, if your hair is bobbed you have to wear a net over it. I notice yours isn't cut." She smoothed her own netted bob. "Personally," she said, "I think it's kind of old-fashioned to keep it long. If you should cut yours, remember to put a net on while you're in the store. Can I do anything for you?"

I pulled myself together, and explained my trip through the store.

"My land," she said, "don't take any of this stuff." She pointed to the pile of fabrics I'd been examining. "Those are all 'as is's.'"

I asked her to repeat what she had just said.

She could scarcely believe, she told me, I didn't know what an "as is" was. "It's merchandise that's marked down," she explained patiently, "because there's something the matter with it. It's got dirty, or maybe some kind of a stain, or a defect in the weaving—something like that. So we pile it up here and give it a big markdown, provided the customer will take it as it is; not ask us to clean it or repair it, or fix it up in any way. It's an 'as is.'"

I thanked her and told her I didn't believe I'd look for anything more just then in the section. "Or any other section," I said to myself. I wanted the haven of my desk where I could add to my Vocabulary List, and at the same time keep the greater part of my brown ensemble out of sight. I had no sooner settled there, crouched so low that my chin barely came over the ledge, when Albert, the Bureau's office boy, came across the aisle and called to me from the railing of our pen. His information, delivered with an unpleasant smile, was that Miss Gardner wanted to see me and had been sending for me every fifteen minutes for the last hour. "You signed out for lunch at twelve-fifteen." It was now two-thirty. "It must have been good. Maybe you didn't

"Those are all 'as-is's.' " I asked her to repeat that.

know when you work here you're only supposed to take an hour."

"I've been working," I told him stiffly. "I'll be right over."

Given my choice of things to do I would have slid under my desk and stayed there. A girl at a near-by desk who had stopped typing to listen to our conversation made a contribution to my day before the boy had got out of earshot. "The timekeeper sent word," she said, "you haven't yet punched the clock. He said to tell you they wouldn't start paying until you started punching." Her voice had carried over a considerable section of the pen. Several girls snickered.

Given another choice of things to do, I would have thrown my Corona in their direction. I got up from my desk, gathering together all the material I had assembled for "Little Things Noticed," but I was so addled by the feeling that everyone was pointing a finger at me and telling me what I had done wrong, I could not immediately find again the trail I had followed to my desk a few minutes before, a different one from the path I'd used in the morning. The girls frequently, I had discovered, shoved and pushed the desks together or apart in varying combinations, following either a whim or perhaps a job requiring close collaboration, I didn't know. Desperate urgency to get out of there and to Miss Gardner prompted me suddenly to stand on my chair, step from there to the top of my desk, cross the other desks like Eliza on the ice, jump down at the gate, push through it, and run across the aisle.

As I waited for Albert to click the door open for me, I realized, agitated as I was, there was not a sound from the pen behind me, not even a typewriter in action. I didn't look round; I bolted through the door the instant it was released.

Miss Gardner was calm but stern. When she'd asked me to sit down she looked at me for a minute without speaking, her eyes traveling the length of my brown dress down to the tips of my brown shoes.

[ 79 ]

I spoke first. "I know," I said, "I ought to be in dark blue or black, but I just found it out."

Miss Gardner nodded. "That's all right," she told me. "I understand. But it is a rule we're very careful to observe up here. You see the rest of the store is a little suspicious of the people in the Advertising Bureau. In the sections they seem to have the idea we do pretty much as we please, and they resent it. That isn't true. Actually we work as hard up here as anybody in the store—harder, I think, than a lot of them. We do have considerable authority. That's one of the reasons we're hired. We're supposed to have a certain amount of taste, and to exercise it in our selection of merchandise and our vetoing of what we don't consider to have style—or taste. We're sort of fashion arbiters."

"Well, my goodness, Miss Gardner," I interrupted, "I haven't vetoed anything."

"I know you haven't," she answered. "But what you have done today is go around the store with a notebook and pencil taking down things about merchandise, without consulting any Buyers."

I wanted to tell her about the Buyers I had encountered the day before and what I'd learned of them from my new friends, but I thought better of it. I didn't say anything.

"The Buyers got wind of it. You might as well know right now that the moccasin telegraph in this store is bigger and more active than the Atlantic Cable. Word got around that somebody was snooping on their merchandise. It couldn't be a comparative shopper because this person didn't have a coat or pocketbook or gloves."

I evidently looked as dim-witted as I felt, because she paused to explain.

"Every store hires a group of women to shop the other stores. They're called comparative shoppers. They look like ordinary customers, but people in the sections can almost always spot them. They report back to their own store what merchandise the others are selling and at what prices. That way every merchant keeps tab on every other merchant, so he won't be caught way off in either a new fashion item or in price. It's a spy system of course, but one that's accepted."

"So," she went on, "when you obviously weren't a comparative shopper, they immediately thought of the Advertising Bureau as the villain. They generally do. They suspected we were sending down a snooper and were going to report to the front office that something, they didn't know what, was wrong with their sections. And they're seething. It wasn't hard to identify the snooper after the first description." Miss Gardner smiled a little. "And then the moccasin telegraph carried the word you were a new member of the *Fashions of the Hour* staff. Since then my telephone hasn't stopped ringing. I know every department you visited. I've had the Buyer from each of them on the wire."

"Oh, Lord," I said, "I'm terribly sorry. I've certainly stirred up a fine mess. I hope you told them I was just a fool. I guess you're going to kick me out."

"Nothing of the sort," Miss Gardner answered briskly. "To begin with, I have a system with Buyers; I recommend it. After I say, 'Hello, this is Miss Gardner speaking,' I let them talk. I don't explain, I don't protest, I don't speak. After a while invariably they say, 'Are you there, Miss Gardner? Am I connected?' I answer I *am* here, they *are* connected, and after that they begin to run down. It's very hard to keep steam up all by yourself, evidently. They taper off, and eventually hang up. Then I hang up. I pass it on to you for what it's worth. It works for me."

She ought to have told me, she continued, to look at the things, carrying them in my mind, come back to my desk, jot them down, go over them with her, then take them to the Buyer to see how plentifully each item was stocked and what the range was in color, size, etcetera.

"You see," she pointed out, "you can't write up a notice about, say, a blue pincushion. Maybe it comes in red, green, pink, purple, etcetera, and in a number of sizes. A reader wants to know all of those things. Or maybe it's a single item a Buyer has picked up with a job-lot of things. There may not be a dozen of them altogether. And suddenly several thousand orders come in from *Fashions of the Hour* readers."

I shuddered. "Dissatisfied customers," I murmured, "by the thousands."

Miss Gardner nodded portentously. "A disaster," she agreed. She became brisk. "Now then," she said, "I think you'd better start over again." This was the second time I'd been advised to start over again. "I've a notice from the Sportswear Department about some new things that have come in from Paris, and by the way, all foreign merchandise is referred to in the store as 'imports.' It may be merchandise from Czechoslovakia or Persia or India, but a Buyer will always refer to it indiscriminately as an import. And by the way, dresses and coats are 'Apparel Sections.'"

I made a mental note to put these on the Vocabulary List.

"Ask for Miss Lacey in the Sportswear. She's very nice. Tell her you'd like to look at the new imports."

I got up to go.

"And be sure to find out," Miss Gardner added, "if they're carrying enough stock on the item to warrant a notice in *Fashions of the Hour*. That's very important."

I asked if she thought it all right for me to go down through the store again in my brown outfit and admitted I'd been stopped by someone in authority. Miss Gardner said it would be all right; she would straighten out the matter, just so I didn't break the rule over again.

I went back to my desk in the conventional way, gathered up notebook and pencil and was about to start out once more when I saw a note tucked under a corner of my typewriter. The upper left-hand corner of the envelope carried the inscription, "Office of the President."

I sat down abruptly. Before I could gather together sufficient courage to open it, I looked around cautiously to see if anyone knew that this communication had been sent me. Several of the girls were eying me furtively. No one had spoken to me while I was threading my way back to my desk; scared into silence themselves, I surmised, by what they knew was waiting for me.

I opened the envelope. Mr. Simpson, the note inside read, would like to see me in his office at four o'clock. Mr. James Simpson was the President of Marshall Field's. In spite of all the things about Field's I did not know, this was one fact of which I was unhappily certain. I looked at my watch. It was two minutes to four.

While I debated the possibility of my ever having sufficient strength after reading this request to accomplish any form of locomotion, a list went through my mind of the things about which he probably wanted to see me. Not punching a time clock, wearing brown instead of blue, forgetting to sign out and then signing out for lunch that seemingly lasted two hours and fifteen minutes, snooping through the store, and leaving my place of business by way of the desk tops.

I knew I ought to be on my way and yet I couldn't seem to get on my feet. In between saying things to myself like "Come on, get it over with, he's only going to fire you," I wondered why Mr. Simpson would bother to fire me. I wasn't important enough to take up a President's time for firing. Anybody could do that, unless the total of my offenses was so great he wanted to give himself the satisfaction of pointing each one out to me.

The girls watched me but no one spoke even to ask what was in the note. I got to my feet and found my way among the desks, glad of their support.

The young man I had seen the day I applied for a job was sitting at the desk just as he'd been before. This was the first time I'd spoken to him, however. "I have a request," I quavered, "from Mr. Simpson. He wants to see me at four o'clock today."

"Come in," he said, pointing to a swinging gate in the railing along the aisle.

I came through it and around to the chair he indicated beside his desk. "Mr. Simpson's busy right now," he said. "I'll take you in as soon as he's free."

I nodded. I didn't want him to hear again how my voice was shaking.

The young man had been writing, copying on a long yellow pad notes and figures from scraps of white paper spread about his desk. He returned to this job. He was stockily built, not tall, but muscular. He wrote vigorously. His hair was more sandy than brown. He had high color in his cheeks and a very clear skin. He was probably not much over twenty, I thought. I hadn't realized I'd been staring at him until he looked up suddenly from his writing and caught my eye. I felt myself blushing and turned away quickly.

"You're scared," he said, "aren't you?" He didn't wait for me to answer. "Everybody is when they come up to see the boss. But don't let it get you down that he's the President. He's a wonderful man."

"I don't need a wonderful man," I said, "to fire me. Anyone would do."

"What makes you think you're going to get fired? Mr. Simpson doesn't fire people. It would have to be something on a big scale for him to do that."

"That's me," I answered and went over the list again in my mind.

A buzzer sounded on the desk between us. The young man got up quickly. "He'll see you now," but he held up a hand as I started to get to my feet by holding onto the desk. "Just wait a minute," he instructed, and walked away.

I got to my feet and leaned against the chair I'd been sitting in. I didn't hear the young man come back until he spoke. "He's ready for you now," he said, and was standing beside me.

"I'm not ready for him," I thought wildly. "All I want is to get out of here and never start all over again anywhere."

I turned and walked beside the young man to a door at the back. The young man opened it but at the threshold stopped. "Mr. Simpson," he said, "this is Miss Kimbrough," and left me.

I saw a man stand up behind a desk at the far end of the room. "Come in, Miss Kimbrough, won't you?" he said.

As I walked the length of the room I remembered a line in Virgil that said, "His hair stood on end and his tongue clove to the roof of his mouth." I couldn't remember how the line went in Latin and I thought to myself this is a fine time to be wondering about Latin. When I got to the desk Mr. Simpson put out his hand and I took it gingerly, afraid that if I availed myself of the support it offered I would sag completely and pull him down to the floor along with me. He indicated an armchair near the desk and I gratefully took the strain off my trembling limbs.

Mr. Simpson sat down at his desk, leaned forward and crossed his hands on top of it. I focused my attention on his hands. I hadn't the courage to look him in the eye. His hands were strong, vigorous, lightly freckled, the fingers blunt, the nails well manicured. "I understand," he said, and I looked up impulsively—his eyes were blue, his hair sandy and he was smiling—"I understand," he repeated, "you've started to work with us in the Advertising Bureau."

"Yes, I have," I found myself able to say and was pleased that I was able.

"That's fine," he broke in rapidly, "we're delighted to have you."

I very nearly rolled off the chair and onto the elegant carpet at his feet.

"Delighted," he repeated, as if he had an intuitive sense I hadn't believed him. If he had, his sense was accurate. I hadn't believed him. "But before you start," he continued, "there are one or two things I want to talk to you about."

Here we go, I thought, on another start, and realized that relief was making me hysterical. I pulled myself together to listen.

He tilted his chair back, crossed one knee over the other and clasped his hands over the knee that was level with the desk. "I want to talk to you about your relationship with the people in this store."

My inner relief began to fade. That moccasin telegraph, I thought. He's heard about my relationship with snooping. I made a sound of interrupting; I wanted to try to explain but he didn't allow me.

"The Buyers," he said hurriedly, "are the most important people in this organization. Never forget that. We executives up here are just the administrators. The Buyers are the life of a department store. They make it. We give our Buyers complete confidence, and complete authority except in such things as concern the organization as a whole."

He uncrossed his knees and leaned forward on the desk again, looking at me intently. "Now these Buyers," he said, "didn't get this confidence and this authority easily, and that's where you come in. They got it the hard way; moving up step by step for a long time over a very long and tough way, because the competition in merchandising is no joke. Most of these people started in the stockroom. And when you start there you're young, just a kid. So they haven't had much education. They haven't had time for it.

"Now let's take a look at the Advertising Bureau. Within the last few years, very few, we've taken into that department young women who've had an education and who've had social advantages, like you. We've never had these young women before; frankly, you're an experiment. I happen to be one of the people who believe that girls like you have a real place in the merchandising world. I think the time will come when there'll be a lot of you in it and occupying very important positions. If," and he emphasized the word by tapping with his forefinger on the desk, "you can get along with the organization, and that means the Buyers. The trouble with most young people who have an education is they think they know a lot. They don't. You don't begin to know what any Buyer knows. I doubt if you'll ever know as much about merchandising as they. But they're suspicious of you and they resent the authority we have to give you in order to allow you to exercise the qualities we hired you for.

"If you go through the store throwing your education in their teeth and generally acting superior, you won't get anything out of them and, what's more, you'll be out of the organization because you won't be of the slightest use to us. But on the other hand, if you can make them feel you have a respect for what they know and a willingness to learn what they can teach you, and show them you're working right along with them for Marshall Field & Company, then I wouldn't be surprised if you got along fine and maybe went a long way. That's all."

He got up abruptly, held out his hand. I stood up and shook it easily this time. "I'm scared of the Buyers," I said, "but I'd like to be friends with them."

"That's all right then," he answered, "I expect you will be."

I'd reached the door when he called, "Oh, just a minute, Miss Kimbrough, I've a note here about something else I wanted to speak to you about."

A note, I thought, that's got on it, dressed in brown, etcetera, and I had only two feet to go to be safely on the other side of the door. The feeling of oozing away came into my limbs again. I looked back. Mr. Simpson was thumbing through a neat pile of memoranda on the desk. He needn't have bothered, it seemed to me. I could have recited the list. I edged closer to the door.

"Here it is," he said. "Oh, yes, I remember now. What do you think about the Hill School?"

For the second time in his office I very nearly dropped to his carpet.

"Do you like it?" he added a little impatiently since I had not answered him. "Your brother's there, isn't he? Mrs. Simpson and I are thinking about boarding schools for young Jim next year. We're considering Hill, and she heard your brother's there. How do you like it?"

"Fine," I said and shot out the door.

The young man at the desk was folding the long sheet on which he'd been writing, into a big envelope. He smiled at me, a charming, open, friendly smile. "Well," he asked, "how did it go? Wonderful man, isn't he?"

"Yes," I said, "he *is*. And he didn't fire me."

"I hardly thought he would," the young man observed dryly.

I was able by now to laugh. "I know," I admitted. "I'm not that important. But I was that scared."

"Sure," he said, "everybody's scared of the President, no matter what kind of a man he is. . . . Well, good luck, Miss Kimbrough."

I paused at the gate. "Thank you ever so much," I said. "You've been awfully nice to me. I don't know what your name is."

"McBain," he said, "Hughston McBain."

To my considerable satisfaction, every girl in my pen stopped typing as I came in. I smiled impartially at them and gave no word about my interview. I looked at my watch and saw it was only four-thirty. There was time, I decided, to see Miss Lacey and get that second new start under way.

With my notebook and pencil I went down to the Sports Section on the sixth floor and asked for Miss Lacey.

Miss Lacey was a big woman, tall, broad-shouldered, heavy, but not fat. Her hair had a reddish tinge that could only have been achieved by asking at the hairdresser's for a henna rinse. She was jovial and kindness itself. In no time we were joking together while she showed me sweaters from London and Scotland, leather belts from Paris to wear with them, little skullcaps from Morocco, with the prices and colors of each at the tip of her tongue. She had just got back from a buying trip abroad and had very little to say in its favor. "You work yourself to death," she complained, "and I hate foreign money—all those centimeters —but you meet nice people on the boats."

When I left she urged me to come again, she'd have a lot more things unpacked in the next few days. I told her I could hardly wait to see them, and we waved good-by to each other.

The elevator I entered had only one other passenger, and that one happened to be Mr. Simpson.

"I'd like to tell you," I blurted out, "that Miss Lacey has just called me 'Ducky Feathers.'"

He chuckled approvingly. "That's a good start," he said.

We reached the ninth floor, the elevator girl opened the door. He waited to let me step out ahead of him and then passed me, walking briskly.

The elevator girl called, "Pssst! Come back here."

I turned, saw she meant me, and walked back. She beckoned me in and closed the door to the elevator.

"I'm just on relief here," she said, "I work on the State Street side. I took this passenger on at the fourth floor. He's the only one in the car and he says to me before we even get to fifth, 'Aren't you new here?' And I tell him, 'What's it *to* you, and don't try to get fresh with me, old man.' Who is the guy?"

"Mr. James Simpson," I told her, "the President of this store."

"Jesus," said the operator. She pushed the lever all the way over and we dropped down to the basement without a stop. Then she turned to me. "I'm sorry," she said, "but you got me rattled."

"That's all right," I told her, "that's all right. You'd just better start all over again."

## * 7 *

AFTER TWO weeks of employment in the store I was, to my family, an authority on Marshall Field & Company. Our conversations at dinner dealt almost exclusively with matters concerning the firm. Mother had many suggestions, such as my insisting that the head of the department selling collars provide fine net in the guimpes mother habitually wore. The last ones, she said, had been of inferior quality. I corrected mother's terminology. A head was a Buyer, a department a section, and the title of that particular section was not Collars but Neckwear.

Mother and father were impressed by my grasp of technical terms. Therefore, I saw no reason to confide that for me to insist on anything from a Buyer would be disastrous. This knowledge was not easy to keep secret when I had tossed to my credulous parents the tidbit that I was at work on an assignment covering the entire store and occupying a whole page in the magazine. Naturally, I did not mention that the title of the page was "Little Things Noticed on a Walk through the Store." They assumed that on such an important mission as a whole page I must command the attention of every Buyer whose department I visited. Even friends of the family's began telephoning me at the store; each one urging a particular request or complaint she wished me to take up with the management.

Since I was not close enough to the management even to warrant my having a telephone of my own, I had to take these calls at Albert's desk. It was hard to convey within his attentive earshot a willingness and an ability to undertake the problems presented without revealing to him the position I was assuming.

When Miss Gardner had seen me several times engaged in these conversations, I confided to her the nature of them. I didn't want her to think I was having social talk during working hours. She was understanding and sympathetic. Every member of the firm, she said, all the way up to the President, had just such demands from people outside the store; complaints, suggestions, requests for information.

"Like a doctor," she asserted, "going out to dinner and being asked by the guests to hear their symptoms. Only that doesn't happen very often to a doctor, and it invariably happens to anyone from Field's. Mr. Corley [he was, I knew, Merchandise Manager] and I were talking about this one day. He said it's because Chicagoans consider Field's belongs to them. They have a personal tie with it that they don't feel about any other store. I think that's because old Mr. Field used to hammer on the importance of the individual customer. You know his slogan, 'Give the lady what she wants.' It's still our slogan today. So our customers sense that relationship and feel the store is theirs. I think Mr. Corley's right," Miss Gardner concluded.

I realized then that in my own circle this interest was not just because I was a girl with a job. I was someone at Field's; therefore I must know all about "their store." I was learning, I hoped, but I needed to find out more, and quickly.

One day passing Mr. Exley's office, I remembered Miss Gardner had said when she'd introduced me to him, "Mr. Exley probably knows more about this store than anyone else in it." In that dim cubbyhole, I realized, sat the answer to my need. I turned round immediately and went back to his open door. No door in the Advertising Bureau was ever closed, though this was one of the few things not a regulation but a custom. No one except Mr. Exley, I had discovered early, stayed at his desk very long at a time; the traffic in and out of every office was almost continuous: copywriters, consulting one another or the Art Department. Only Mr. Exley remained at his desk; he was the funnel all this hurly-burly narrowed into on its way to print.

I tapped against his open door to attract his attention from the page proofs spread out on his desk under a lamp. I asked if I might see him some time during the day when he wasn't busy. He invited me in instantly, insisting there was no urgency about the proofs he was reading since they were not for newspaper ads but inserts to go out with the bills to charge customers the following month.

When I told him my need for statistics about the store, his eyes gleamed and he rubbed his hands with pleasure. "Of course, of course," he said, "every employee of this store is a representative of Marshall Field & Company. And Marshall Field & Company is the largest retail organization of its kind in the world, and by organization I mean the retail store and the wholesale branch. In the matter of the seat of authority the retail store is perhaps a branch of the wholesale; then there are the factories that manufacture Marshall Field products, and all the foreign offices."

Listening, I thought, "There are people in this store—and in the short time I've been here I've already encountered several of them—who are like teakettles on a stove. Say 'Marshall Field & Company' and it's like lighting a match and turning on the gas under them. In no time they're at the boil."

I paid attention again to Mr. Exley.

". . . more than an organization, of course," he was saying. "It's a great institution, and unique, not another one like it." He paused, "Except, perhaps, Mr. Wanamaker's store in Philadelphia." He did not concede this easily; I counted it a triumph of accuracy over reluctance. "Field's is one of the wonders of Chicago," he continued hastily and in a louder tone. "Travelers come from all over the world to see this institution."

"He's really on the boil now," I thought. "This is where the lid begins to bounce," and he did start tapping on the desk with a thick blue pencil.

"You will find, Miss Kimbrough, that everyone who comes here to work begins to feel within a very short time a sense of personal responsibility, just like your coming to me today. And you're not in the least unusual. I don't suppose you have any idea how often and how many employees come to me for information because, they say, customers in the store and people they meet outside are always asking about Field's.

"You see what a personal pride almost every employee has. So instead of answering these questions with an 'I don't know,' they come to me to find out, just like you. People here get the feeling the store in a way belongs to them, and they also feel a cut above anyone who works, but doesn't work at Field's. You know this was the first store women came into as clerks, because they considered Field's so respectable."

I said I had a feeling even people who didn't work in the store, that were just customers, looked on Field's in a sort of proprietory manner.

Mr. Exley agreed vigorously. "They tell me at the Complaint Desk," he declared, "that over and over a woman will say, 'I didn't expect this of Field's.' "

"As if," I put in, "it were a member of the family that had been a disappointment."

"That's it," Mr. Exley agreed, "and I venture to say there isn't a citizen of Chicago that doesn't bring an out-of-town visitor to Field's as just about the first sight to see on a tour of the city. Now they tell me," he continued, "that isn't so in New York. I understand there isn't a store there that matches up in sight-seeing to the Metropolitan Museum or Grant's Tomb. But in

Chicago it's Marshall Field's, the Art Institute, the Stockyards and the Field Museum."

I brought the conversation back to the matter of statistics. Mr. Exley apologized for having digressed from it, explaining that when he started talking about the store he got carried away. If I would come back to him at the end of the day he would have some material for me I might find useful.

That night there were guests for dinner, and I tossed into the middle of the soup course the news that the main store of Marshall Field & Company comprised 13 stories and 3 basements, the height above street level 219 feet 2 inches, the depth below street level 43 feet 4 inches. The total area of the main store was 1,966,320 square feet; the store for men, directly across Washington Street from the main store, devoted 234,551 square feet and 6 floors to men's wear. Furthermore, the basement underneath the main store, Washington Street, and the store for men totaled approximately 1¼ city blocks and included 82 selling sections. It also boasted its own corps of Buyers.

This announcement was greeted by cries of wonder from the guests and a look of dazed stupefaction on the face of each of my parents. In the silence that followed, while the guests rallied for a return to the separate conversations I had interrupted with my *bombe surprise* I overheard the gentleman on mother's right remark that he considered my mastery of figures remarkable. I overheard mother's reply too; that she considered it even more remarkable than he, remembering as she did the up-to-midnight hours she had spent coaching me on figures or dates for examinations in either Mathematics or History, and that, had she been asked, she would have guaranteed the only figures I knew were that pi was 3.1416 and the Battle of Hastings 1066.

When the vegetables were being passed I observed, from Mr. Exley's notes concealed on my lap under the napkin, that at Marshall Field & Company were 65 windows on the street level, presenting a panorama of color in artistry, fabric and

I asked the gentleman on my left . . .

fashion that had won renown the world over. The prose as well as the figures were Mr. Exley's. I considered them equally effective.

And I was right. The effect was silence all around the table. I broke it myself by vouchsafing that the telephone exchange, State 1000, the Marshall Field & Company number, was one of the largest privately operated switchboards anywhere, with 105 outgoing trunk lines, 250 incoming. The switchboard had been known to handle over 35,000 calls in one day.

While this was sinking in, I asked the gentleman on my left if he knew that we—I emphasized the pronoun—had a permanent staff of 9,500 employees and that it increased to 15,000 at the Christmas season. It was purely a rhetorical question. While he was mumbling, as I had anticipated, about indeed not knowing any of these things, I bounced in again with the suggestion that perhaps he did not know either that approximately 100,000 customers entered *our* store during a normal selling day, and during a Christmas rush a tally by *our* Research Bureau had revealed a total of a quarter of a million customers on one day.

Mother interrupted me by calling my name, but I rose above it. The daily average for people served in *our* tearooms on the seventh floor was, in December, 10,273, but on one particular Saturday in December, 13,945 customers had eaten there.

Mother spoke my name a little more urgently but she needn't have been concerned. I had come to the end of Mr. Exley's notes.*

That week end I went to Lake Forest to stay with friends. It was not, as I said to mother at seven-thirty on Saturday morning, what I would once have called a week end. I was saying good-by to her, suitcase in hand, on my way to the store and due there promptly at eight-thirty; but I would not be released until half-

---

* The statistics given are of 1950. My memory for figures is no more accurate now than it was then. I must still rely on notes. These were supplied by the current Advertising Bureau.

past five. It would be seven o'clock by the time I reached Lake Forest.

Saturday night I went to a dance, but even there some people asked me about my job. Sunday morning they began again. I didn't volunteer Marshall Field information but I was asked for it. On the tennis court a racket would be leveled at me and the owner demand without preamble, "How large is the Tiffany mosaic dome that is one of the outstanding features of Marshall Field & Company?"

"One million six hundred thousand pieces," I would answer without an instant's hesitation.

Or perhaps, "Is there a separate store laundry and how big is it?"

The answer to that one was, "There is, and it handles thirty-five thousand pieces daily. The service is for store purposes only."

The questions were well put and they did not exceed my range of knowledge for the reason that the guests had taken possession of Mr. Exley's notes I had brought with me in case I should find opportunity to use them. These were the friends who, only a short time ago, had coached me over the week end in rendering on the typewriter, "Now is the time for all good men to come to the aid of their party." We were, they felt, advancing together in Marshall Field & Company.

The following week Mr. Exley hailed me timidly as I passed his hole-in-the-wall one morning. He had spoken, he said, to Miss Helen Duggan, the head of Basement Underwear—in the store it was called "Lanjeray"—and told her I was interested in facts about Field's. She had sent word she'd be glad to see me if I would come at a time when she was not busy. That would have to be early morning. She could tell me, Mr. Exley promised, a great many things because she'd been an employee for a long time.

I came into the store early the next morning and went down immediately I had checked in, to see her. I was in some trepidation about talking to a Buyer, but she was friendly at once. She couldn't imagine, she said crisply, but chuckled as she said it, that any of the young flibbertigibbets they had upstairs now would be interested in hearing how the store used to be. But there certainly was a lot she could tell.

I assured her I was interested, without elaborating that my motive was not so much personal acquirement of knowledge as a sudden vista of social success to be achieved if I could learn to use knowledge with appropriate timing.

She leaned against a counter and began to talk. She was just out of high school, she said, in 1904, when she'd come to work at Marshall Field's. Her first job had been selling side combs in the Jewelry Department during the Christmas rush. At the end of her first day she had seen a fine-looking man in a Prince Albert coat and hard hat, standing on the landing of the stairs looking over the Jewelry Department. She had left her table and gone immediately up to him. "Are you Mr. Marshall Field?" she had asked.

A little taken aback, he had answered, "I am."

"Well," she had told him, "this is my first day here and I thought you'd like to know I think this is a fine store." Then she'd gone back to her table.

She stopped to laugh herself at this recollection, took off her glasses, wiped them, replaced them and then continued. At the end of the Christmas season she'd been kept on because she'd gone to the General Manager on the ninth floor and had sent in word it was important for her to see him. She had been admitted and had said, "I've got my notice to leave here tomorrow. If I go it will be a bad mistake for Field's. This is what I've sold in twenty-three days," and handed him her sales figures. He'd studied them gravely and told her she could stay.

She'd been put then in the "Come Back Window" in "Alterations" in the Women's Wear Department. Her job there had been to take garments returned, call the fitter and try to make adjustments. If that failed she had taken the garment to the Buyer. "You know the rule, 'Give the lady what she wants'?"

I acknowledged I'd heard it.

"So if the customer didn't want what the Buyer had to offer," Miss Duggan resumed, "she could return her purchase no matter how much alteration had been made on it. But my Buyer, Mrs. Cox, didn't take to this rule. A czarina; and she'd get boiling mad when I'd bring these garments to her. But she didn't dare show the customer she was mad, you can believe, so she'd take it out on me. It was good training.*

"There were five Women's Department heads in those years," Miss Duggan continued, "who practically ran the store. Each one of them had groups of sections under her. They'd dress in fine style and sweep down the aisles with their long trains swishing. You had to step aside when they passed. They were high and mighty."

From there she'd been drafted against her wishes into the Basement Underwear Section and not long after that had been made an assistant to the Buyer, Mrs. Wardell. But when Mrs. Wardell had wanted some months later to send Miss Duggan to New York to buy Infants' Wear, the Merchandise Manager, looking over her hundred pounds and general schoolgirl appearance, had pronounced her too young. To meet this temporary setback, Mrs. Wardell had taken her in hand, bought her a $120 black satin dress, fixed her hair up high and returned her to the Merchandise Manager. Astonished at the change in her, he'd given permission at once for her to go.

Armed with this outfit, Miss Duggan had set out on her first buying trip, holding fast the advice Mrs. Wardell had emphasized: "Always wear white gloves, always ask for the owner of

* Returned merchandise at Field's is probably greater than in any other store, not because of inferior merchandise, but adhering to the policy of "Give the lady what she wants." Many million dollars' worth of goods were returned in 1950. The store works constantly to reduce this, but not by restricting returns.

the business, always say, 'I'm from Marshall Field & Company. I want to see your line.'"

Miss Duggan had been frightened by New York but not too frightened to buy $8,000 worth of goods. "And by the third day—" when she told me this she smiled a little—"I saw what the name of Marshall Field & Company did, and that relaxed me."

By 1915 Miss Duggan was the head of the section. Mrs. Wardell had left because an over-all head of the basement had been installed and Mrs. Wardell had not taken kindly to the idea of being bossed by anyone. "She was a powerful personality," Miss Duggan described her, "and those women Buyers stuck together, I can tell you. Marcella Hahner," she added, "is the last of that group: beautifully dressed, bossy, selling goods at a fast clip—crack merchants."

Mr. Shedd, President of Field's when Mr. Simpson was Vice-President, had sent Miss Duggan on her first buying trip abroad, to the Philippines to spend $500,000 on Infants' Wear for the Retail and the Wholesale stores. In the getting of it she had gone by motor into the jungle, taking guides and a native chauffeur who slept with the guides while she slept in the car at night, locking it up carefully from the inside.

When orders had not come through as fast as she thought they should, she'd tracked them down into settlements deep in the jungle, and many times found her inventory, as she called it, all over the villages; on houses, fences, bushes, put out temporarily as decoration for some Feast Day.

After the Philippines she'd gone to China and Japan. "They were interesting countries too," she said. "I got along fine."

I ask about the change from cotton and linen to silk underwear.

She put up her hand before her face and shook her head. "Oh my," she groaned, "the trouble we had with David Yates over that." David Yates was in my simpler ken the terrifying Vice-President of Marshall Field's. "The first thing I put out on the counter, just to try it one day, was a little pink bodice made of satin. Dave Yates came along and ordered it off on the spot. 'That's too Frenchy,' he said, 'it's immoral.' Mind you, other stores on the street had been carrying silk underwear for some time, but I must say in the beginning only the girls from the Eversleigh and such clubs, and their Madames, bought it. They bought heavily though and Field's didn't get their silk underwear business. I said to Yates, 'Your daughter wears that.' And he came back at me, 'She won't after I get home tonight.' But I guess she did because he never came back and I went on displaying the underwear and selling it.

"But when it came to a kind named Figleaf, that was silk with a sort of leaf to fasten it together, Yates was frightened nearly out of the store. And he wouldn't let us sell it under that name. But now he's kind of hardened to the whole idea, I guess. We've got silk negligees and slips along with the best of them.

"I still buy from the Philippines and Japan and China, but I get Paris underwear too. And I can tell you it's always exciting to me to go on a foreign trip, especially because of the attention I get by representing Field's. There isn't another store in the world that allows its people to buy such large amounts of merchandise without having to get confirmation from home. That makes you feel like somebody."

I urged her to tell me more about Mr. Yates.

"He'll back you to the limit," she said, "but he's tough to get a raise out of." She leaned forward confidentially. "Do you know it wasn't too long ago I was doing a million-dollar business a year and getting thirty-five dollars a week with a measly bonus of a few hundred dollars a year. I guess you know the top salary in the store is six thousand dollars a year, except Shedd and Simpson. Buyers make their extra on bonus and commission and we scratch for it.

"Shedd is a great merchant. When he was President, he'd never let a day go by without he'd go all through the store looking at merchandise. He always picked it up and felt it. He knew quality like nobody I ever saw. He'd always ask, 'How much did you pay for it? What are you asking?' His voice was high and a little squeaky, but what he said was sound.

"I remember once in the early days I mentioned to him I worked on the job until two o'clock every night getting my reports and accounts in shape. I guess I thought that would impress him with what a valuable employee I was. You know what he said? He said, 'I think the job's too big for you. You ought to be able to close your books at six o'clock and then have some fun. If you can't do that, you're not up to this.' I quit that night at six, let me tell you, and I've done it ever since.

"You know Simpson?" she asked suddenly.

"I've met him," I told her.

"He's a wonderful man," she said emphatically. "He's been one of the best business friends I've ever had. He's square, he has a good sense of humor, though he doesn't show it to many people. And let me tell you, he's got a keen brain. He doesn't let many people come close to him, but we get along fine. He says I'm a good housekeeper. I am, too. I think that's one of the most important ways to sell merchandise. I'm after my salespeople all the time. 'Keep the merchandise folded,' I tell them. 'Keep it clean, keep it neat. One soiled sample can ruin your whole stock.'"

She reverted to Simpson. "He's got snap judgment. Quick, to the point," she asserted. "Once I came back from a trip and told him I had to have more money. He said, 'How much do you want?' and I told him. You know what he answered?" She shook her head. "He said, 'I think you're worth more than that, but that's all you asked for and that's what I'm going to give you. You asked for it. You'll get it, but nothing more.' But he's boosted me right along since then. I can't complain."

Miss Duggan's assistant came up with a request and an apology for interrupting. I said I was the one who should apologize for taking up so much of Miss Duggan's time, and turned to go.

"Come back whenever you want to," Miss Duggan called after me. "I'll talk your head off any time."

One day that week Miss Elizabeth Faulkner dined with us. She was the head of the Faulkner School for Girls from which I had graduated. She was the most brilliant teacher I ever had and my friend. But she was a powerful talker and accustomed to dominating a school assembly.

We had come out from dinner when she said to me, "I'm so interested in your having a real job, Emily, and at Marshall Field's. One of the things I should think would be fascinating is the variety of people with whom you must come in contact."

This was my cue and I swelled to it.

"I do," I said quickly, "and I met one of the most fascinating people just this week. Her name is Miss Duggan." But I had reckoned without Miss Faulkner.

"It's a pity," she said, "you never knew old Mr. Marshall Field. He was a wonderful character. I remember him as a little girl very well. My mother met him when she came as a bride to Chicago, because he had lived with a group of young bachelors— my father one of them at the time—in a boarding house."

"Miss Duggan met him the first day she went to work at Field's," I interpolated hopefully.

"We were members of the same church," Miss Faulkner continued, and Miss Duggan and I faded away. "The First Presbyterian Church at Twenty-first and Indiana Avenue. Mr. Leiter, Mr. Field's original partner, as all old Chicagoans know," and that eliminated the Kimbroughs, "had the other half of the Faulkner pew.

"Many people," Miss Faulkner was well launched now, "considered Mr. Field a hard man. This was not so. We knew him to be very kind, and looking back on it now, I realize how broadminded he was and how ahead of his day. I heard him say, 'Narrowness is a thing no one can stand in religion.' He was very fond of our clergyman, Dr. Barrows, and worked out with him a Parliament of Religions that was held at the World's Fair. They brought representatives from all over the world; to bring any tribes that had the dignity of formal ritual was their goal. And Mr. Field withdrew later from the church in protest because the deacons refused permission to Dr. Barrows to go to India and China on a lecture tour, because they could see no value in such a trip."

"Miss Duggan," I suggested hurriedly, "made a trip to the Philippines and to Japan and China for the store."

"He was thoughtful of his employees, too."

I wondered dismally if by raising my hand I could win her attention but decided against it.

"I remember very well," Miss Faulkner had the attention of everyone, "a young clerk at the ribbon counter. Mr. Lindstrom was his name. He always waited on my mother and she bought a great many ribbons, because she had eight daughters. She had one son, too, but he didn't count at the ribbon counter."

We all laughed, but not enough to interrupt. "One winter my mother was distressed to find that Mr. Lindstrom seemed unable to shake off a persistent cold. Each time she went—and he always saw to it there was a stool for her—she found him coughing badly. Finally one day she spoke to him about it and he told her he couldn't seem to throw off the cough because the counter was near an entrance, and the door opening blew on him. That very day my mother met Mr. Field in another part of the store. He stopped to speak to her as he always did, and asked about the family. And she told him about Mr. Lindstrom's cough and how courteous he was. She felt, she declared, he ought to be in another place. The very next time she went in to shop, and she went to the ribbon counter, Mr. Lindstrom said, 'Mrs. Faulkner, this is my last day here. I'm to take charge of the seating arrangements in the tearoom. Somebody told Mr. Field about my cough.'"

In the murmur of appreciation that followed, I tried once more.

"Miss Duggan said," I inserted hurriedly, "Mr. Field established the policy of putting more responsibility on employees, especially Buyers and Section Managers, than any other merchandising business. That's how *she* had so much power."

Miss Faulkner smiled. "Emily," she said, and I stopped. "You would be particularly interested in this. I think my mother was responsible for the establishment of one of the largest departments in the store." I sat back again. "One day," she continued, "mother was shopping in the fabric section and met Mr. Field there. After a few minutes of pleasant chat and answering his questions about the health of each one of the family—and he remembered the name of every one of the eight girls—my mother said to him, 'Mr. Field, you have become more than a drygoods store now. You have beautiful ready-made things for women. I don't need a dressmaker for myself any more. But why don't you have ready-made clothes for my children? With eight daughters, I have a seamstress in the house almost the year round. If I could outfit them here I should consider that a major blessing.' And Mr. Field answered, 'Mrs. Faulkner, I'm going to think this over very seriously.'

"We have always felt," Miss Faulkner concluded triumphantly, "that the whole fourth floor, the young people's floor, stemmed from my mother's request."

In the exclamations that followed and assurances that this must be so, she made a move to go and the party ended. We were turning out the lights in the living room when mother asked, "What did you start to tell tonight about a Miss Duggan?"

"I wouldn't tell you now for the world," I said. "The Duggan story's bound to come round."

# * 8 *

AT THE end of a week in the store I had gathered material for the page, "Little Things Noticed on a Walk . . ." I had skirted round the Buyers as much as possible but I had at arm's length got their sanction of the merchandise I wanted to use. Miss Gardner went over with me my notes on all the items I had selected, and then sent me on my rounds once more to check again a guarantee that this merchandise would be taken off sale and held back until the magazine came out, and assurance of a sufficient supply to take care of orders from the magazine readers.

This took nearly two weeks and almost countless trips, because of the difficulty of meeting with a Buyer, physically and temperamentally. Miss Gardner assured me I must not look on this as the standard of procedure for newspaper advertising—that had to be done on the double, from collecting merchandise to the finished proof. But *Fashions of the Hour* was special, and since it came out only six times a year, we could allow ourselves a longer period of preparation; though she warned that at the end, when we were ready to go to press, we would be involved in as big a rush as the newspaper people went through daily.

"The Buyers," she explained, "hate to hold back merchandise because a quick turnover is a mark of successful buying. But on the other hand they love to be represented in *Fashions of the*

[    107    ]

*Hour* because it means prestige and a wider range of customers than the daily in-the-store shoppers."

She suggested I go first to see the Personal Shopping Service in action, in order to learn at first hand something of how the store tried to satisfy a customer and what it took to provide that satisfaction. I went by way of Mr. Exley to ask how this service had started.

He could tell me, he said happily, as indeed I knew he could. It had begun when a derby-hatted bewhiskered LaSalle Street broker driving in his carriage to work had stopped at Field's on an errand for his wife. He'd found the store not yet opened and so had scrawled on the back of his calling card, "Baby needs new shoes, size two. And the Madame wants spool of thread to match attached sample." His coachman had pinned the card and attached sample to Charley's Door. Charley had filled the order himself that day, handing the package to the coachman when the carriage drew up as the store was closing.

The next day Charley had found three notes on the door from friends of the broker, the following day, eight. And after that the Personal Shopping Service was begun.

I found it to be a large room filled, except for communicating aisles, with rows of girls seated at telephone switchboards and facing two large screens suspended from the ceiling against a wall. The head of the Service told me every operator received daily a mimeographed sheet of the day's advertised items. On these sheets the items were described more fully than in the newspaper advertisement, because customers could think of many more things to ask than there was space for in the advertising copy. Reports on the changing supply of these items were flashed almost constantly on the screen; such as, "Size 10 out in all colors—Size 12 out in yellow."

The girls answered a phone call by saying, "May I help you?" One of the two or three supervisors to whom I talked said the girls formerly had answered calls with "Personal Shopping Service." It had been changed because many times a customer wanted to complain and thought she'd got the wrong desk. "That," the inspector looked a little frightened at such a prospect, "sometimes annoyed the customer." Therefore the girls expressed only a desire to help, and took complaints, passing them on to the proper adjustment bureaus or giving out information they were sure of. Stumped by requests for such things as timetable information on trains to California, and rates for shipping a dog to Hawaii, a girl would reroute those queries to the Travel Bureau on the third floor, and return to taking an order for anything from one spool of thread to be sent to Lake Forest, Special Delivery, because the customer wanted to finish a dress to wear for dinner that night, to a Chinese manservant to be interviewed, and if, in Field's estimation, found satisfactory, put on a train, destination a New York customer. Sables, I was told, and the most expensive jewelry had been ordered by telephone, as well as a five-cent Valentine to be selected "for my mother."

Following the dictum of Mr. Marshall Field, the slogan of the Personal Shopping Service was, a supervisor explained proudly, "We'll deliver a needle and we'll pick it up." She boasted further that it took a good deal to surprise this Service, but admitted the department had been a little dazed only the week before my visit when a customer had telephoned from a railroad station in Kansas City. The customer was somewhat agitated but had turned to Field's for help. She was on her way East from the Coast, she had explained somewhat breathlessly, had changed trains at Kansas City and learned there that all the baby's equipment, including a nursery icebox with bottles of the baby's formula, had been put on a wrong train and one that had already left Kansas City by the time she had discovered the error. Would the Shopping Service please buy other equipment, and she outlined the items needed, make up the stipulated number of bottles, and she dictated the formula, put them in a nursery icebox packed in ice, and deliver the whole to her when she got in to the Dearborn Street Station? The Shopping Service had filled the order.

Another supervisor, overhearing this recital, modified the record of the department a little by admitting to some mistakes. One customer ordering a vase had got a bag of marbles. Another requesting a color chart for paint had received a black corset. And only that morning a desperate plea had come from a customer who, having ordered a fruitcake from the tearoom bakery department, had not received it, but on reordering had, up to the time of her morning telephone call, received eight fruitcakes.

I was in something of a daze when I left the Personal Shopping Service, but I rallied sufficiently to recheck throughout the store the stock of every piece of merchandise destined for my *Fashions of the Hour* page.

Satisfied with this, Miss Gardner's comment was, "All right. Now write it."

And I was face to face with my typewriter and my first writing assignment, not counting—and I chose not to count it—my story that had been whittled to a single-line caption. I wanted to continue indefinitely selecting merchandise, to return fifty times for rechecking, to go on errands for all the people in the Bureau, even to meet Buyers I hadn't heretofore encountered and see again those I had. Anything, rather than write. There was, I knew dismally as I stared at the typewriter, no possibility of my keeping a job along those lines.

No one was happy about my career as it came off the machine. An enveloping ignorance of the way advertising should be written, and perhaps a persistent memory in the back of my mind of the Stationery Buyer and his gold watch, brought out of me a page done in the manner of *Alice in Wonderland*.

Miss Gardner was the first to express doubt about it. She was the first person who saw it. "We've never had advertising done in a humorous vein," she said.

"I don't think it's very humorous," I assured her mournfully.

"Perhaps not," was her answer, spoken kindly, "but I'm sure you meant it to be." She read it a second time while I sat beside her, sweating. I could think of nothing in all my life—and I tried to, as I sat there—not even Bryn Mawr College entrance examinations, that had exercised on me the fine torture provided by sitting and watching someone read words I had written. After what seemed like the time it takes one to drown, Miss Gardner looked up from the page and across at me. "I'm going to follow the Field policy," she said, "and take it. Everybody who gets a job here in the store is allowed to hang himself, and the management backs him all the way, while he's either achieving or avoiding that end. We've never run this kind of copy before, but I know I can get Mr. Schaeffer to go along with me on it, only you'll have to sell it to the merchandise people."

A kinder verdict would have been to turn down the piece, but that was not Miss Gardner's way. She accepted it and only sent Daniel Kimbrough right back again into the lions' den.

Mr. Tracy did not take it kindly that in return for a bottle of Blue Rose I should hand him an exposition of the fragance entitled, "Take Care of the Scents and the Sounds Will Take Care of Themselves." He was not so angry as he was incredulous and grieved. He asked me to come back of the section to his desk. I think he felt a need to sit down and at a place of authority. There he took paper and pencil and worked laboriously and silently for perhaps ten minutes while I stood facing him. At the end of that time he turned the paper round, pushed it toward me and said, "This is more what I had in mind. I think you'll find it will catch the eye and make a snappy ad."

I read, "Blue Rose is the perfume choice of those who love fine things."

I assured him this was a catchy caption, but better perhaps for a newspaper than for the magazine. In my experience, I said, I had learned—but I did not tell him I had learned this only the preceding day and that my total experience was contained in the piece he was reading—"I have learned," I repeated emphatically, "that the principle in newspaper advertising must be that 'he who runs may read.'" But a magazine was a bit of reading that stayed on the living-room table and was gone over at leisure, perhaps reread several times; therefore you wanted something provocative in the caption that would lead on into the body of the piece, rather than tell the whole story at first glance.

Mr. Tracy shook his head but conceded mournfully that he would read on into the piece. The first line under the caption was, "Said the Duchess." That stopped him. It was not difficult to determine just where Mr. Tracy was in his reading because he formed with his lips each word as he came to it. He looked up, his eyes brightened, a happy smile spread over his face. "Well," he said, "that's not such a bad little ad after all."

There were eight paragraphs to my story—perfumes that month had been given the center spread with a cut. Mr. Tracy didn't read any of the paragraphs. He only ran his pencil down the page, stopping at each mention of a specific brand and price, nodding, "That's right, that's right." Reaching the bottom of the page and the end of the piece, he wrote a large OK and his signature under it. He handed it back to me across the desk and stood up. As I passed him on my way to the door he gave my shoulder a friendly little tap. "Bringing in our Carriage Trade like that," he said, "right at the top of your story. That's a good seller."

Until I took the copy for his OK, I had never met Mr. Harris of the second floor. He had been abroad on a buying trip when I'd gathered the merchandise and I had worked with his assistant, Jean Schureman. It was his opinion, Mr. Harris stated vehemently, that the assistant and I between us had betrayed him personally and done Marshall Field & Company no good. In the first place he had items that moved much faster than sundials, birdbaths, silk-covered celluloid desk sets and baskets for sugar bowl and cream pitcher. He didn't want to take up space advertising such items. "If," he added bitterly, "you can call advertising a thing that begins:

" 'Two days wrong. I told you butter wouldn't suit the works,' said the Mad Hatter gloomily." A sundial is the only safeguard against such mechanical difficulties . . . etcetera.

He looked up at this point, raised his eyebrows, shrugged his shoulders, resumed reading, and at the end of the passage observed bitingly, "I'm surprised you bothered to put in the prices." He handed back to me the sheet on which this was written and read again the second item:

"The bath was quite crowded. There was a duck, a dodo, a lory, and an eaglet." You might make just such an interesting, though different, collection with a birdbath . . . etcetera.

He wore the expression of one who has had put under his nose a particularly unpleasant odor. "You know what that will bring, don't you? Complaints from customers that our birdbaths haven't got dodos, lories and eaglets to go with them." He returned that page to me, holding it gingerly as if it were the source of the unpleasant odor.

The next one began:

" 'I shall sit here on and off for days,' said the Frog Footman." And so will everyone who plants a garden. A kneeling pad of oilcloth . . . etcetera.

His comment as he handed that one back to me was, "Our customers are certainly going to like being compared to frogs."

When he had finished reading:

" 'Why in a basket?' 'Why not?' said the Dormouse." And so the cream pitcher and sugar bowl are transported from tea wagon to tea guest in a basket especially designed for them . . . etcetera.

"Why don't you write advertising for the Zoo?" was Mr. Harris's comment as he returned the page.

And for:

"Why is a raven like a writing desk?" No answer—but as to why a desk set for your guest room—you'll know that when you see those of silk covered with celluloid . . . etcetera.

"Now," he said, "we're doing children's riddles. They might like that on the fourth floor. Miss Kimbrough, it seems to me you don't know just where you belong."

I felt he had a point there but I didn't acknowledge it.

He took the pages back from me and riffled through them. "Did Miss Gardner see these?" he asked.

"Yes," I said eagerly, "and liked them." I knew this was pushing her comment but I was being pushed too.

Mr. Harris skimmed over the pages again. "Well," he said finally, "I don't know what on earth she's thinking of. But I have respect for Miss Gardner's judgment. She's a lady."

It had not before occurred to me that the two were synonymous, but I concurred enthusiastically.

"And," Mr. Harris continued, while I held my breath, "since I wasn't here in the beginning to set you straight about the merchandise, I guess I'll just have to OK these." He wrote the OK and his signature on each page.

On my way out of the section I ran into Mr. Schureman. He was waiting for me behind a display table that concealed us from Mr. Harris. "Did you get by?" he asked.

I showed him proudly the OK. Mr. Schureman told me I was lucky.

"I believe you," I assured him.

He invited me to come down to the section again. There were a lot of good stories there, he said, adding that he'd gathered from our conversations while we were collecting merchandise I was fascinated by what went on in the store.

He'd guessed exactly right, I told him, and I'd come down any chance I got.

I went off gaily. Mr. Schureman had been easy to talk to and pleasant to work with.

"All anyone needed to say was, 'Beautiful petit point . . .' "

A few minutes later I was glad I had had the Schureman interlude. A Buyer on the first floor was standing in front of me,
rattling my entire sheaf of papers in one hand and thumping them
with the other. He had taken them all from me after reading those
I'd handed him that pertained to his department. He wanted to
see, he had said, if it was possible I had written about other departments as I had about his. Discovering I had, he announced
vociferously his inability to convey to me what I was doing to
Marshall Field & Company, and certainly to him. As if I had
never seen any of them before, he read aloud in a trembling voice:

"'Adventures first, explanations take such a dreadful time,' said the
Gryphon." They need not if the passport is always ready in a leather
case . . . etcetera.

At the end of the reading he opened and closed his mouth a
few times, struggling, I was uncomfortably sure, to express his
comment. He went on to the next paper, throwing the first to
the floor.

"You couldn't deny, even if you tried with both hands"—that a keycase
of soft leather with gold mountings . . . etcetera.

This page followed the first to the floor.

"'Must a name mean something?' Alice asked," was his next
selection. "Well, petit point . . . has come to mean the newest
thing in its combination with leather . . . etcetera."

As that page drifted to the floor he observed, and his voice
sounded as if he were strangling, "Those beautiful cigarette and
glove boxes I had made especially in Italy. All anyone needed to
say was, 'Beautiful petit point and tooled leather boxes—first
floor, Wabash Avenue,' and you would have had all Chicago, at
least all of Chicago that matters, *flocking* in to my department.
But instead they hire up there in the Advertising Bureau someone
who deliberately makes fun of my merchandise."

I tried to protest this but he drowned me out with the vehe-
mence of his next reading selection:

" 'They lived in an academy.' 'What did they live on?' asked Alice, always interested in questions of eating and drinking.
'They lived on the crops,' answered the Dormouse.
'It was a riding academy.' "
A slender crop of black leather . . . etcetera.

By the end of this reading the Buyer had recovered from his strangling attack. His voice instead took on the tone of a train-announcer. "Marshall Field & Company," he declaimed, "always stands for the finest quality in merchandise and dignity in presenting it. I should like to inquire, young lady, just who you think you are that you can flout, yes flout, such traditions. Can you answer me?"

I tried but I was unnerved. My voice came out like the squeak of a French locomotive. I said that Field's, I thought, had also stood for what was new and different. I hadn't meant to make fun of any of the merchandise. I was only trying to give its presentation a slightly different style.

The Buyer interrupted with a loud noise, expressing dissatisfaction with this explanation.

Miss Bredin came into my view down the aisle. She was almost on the run. Catching my eye, she lifted her arm and waved encouragingly to me. Someone, I realized, must have got word to her what was going on. She was to my fond eye the Northwest Mounties, the messenger galloping into the prison courtyard with a reprieve from the governor, and, when she spoke, St. Cecelia. "I hear," were the words she said, "Miss Kimbrough's done a little stunt for the magazine that's going to tickle our Carriage Trade."

Had Miss Bredin's announcement been that Mr. Simpson, the President of Marshall Field's, was scheduled that morning to do a fandango under the Tiffany dome, my opponent would have received the news with scarcely greater righteous horror. His jaw dropped, his eyes bulged slightly. "Since when," he inquired and his voice cracked on the query, "has Marshall Field & Company wished to tickle its customers?"

"It's a new style," Miss Bredin assured him soothingly, "one of our girls got it from a friend in Perfumes. Tracy over there says one of his finest customers let herself be quoted in the ad, a *Duchess*."

I silently but fervently promised Mr. Tracy I would, provided I wasn't fired in the meantime, write him an ad one day on Blue Rose perfume that would bring tears of happiness to his eyes.

Miss Bredin's boss pulled his watch from his pocket, looked at it, and gave a start. "Good gracious," he said, "they'll have my whole French shipment unpacked without my seeing it. I should be up in the stockroom this minute. You've wasted a good deal of my time, young lady," he added severely, "give me those pages."

Until this command I hadn't dared acknowledge the existence of the pages on the floor. I squatted down, scooped them together in my hands and handed them to him. I watched, scarcely daring to breathe, his signature over an OK go on every one of them. When he had written his signature on the last one, he gave the sheaf back to me, pulled his watch out again, clucked his tongue in annoyance at what he read, and scurried off without another word.

As I turned to go I said to Miss Bredin, "I'll never be able to thank you enough for what you did today."

"That's all right," she answered and her voice was brisk, "if Marshall Field's hadn't given young people a chance to hang themselves, the store wouldn't be where it is today. Anyway, I told the truth. They tell me Tracy's crowing like a rooster over his ad. Got anything for me?"

I pulled out a sheet from the pile and handed it to her over my shoulder. She read it aloud:

"If I am not the same, who in the world am I?" For just such problems of identity, there is fashionable stationery with monogram to the left, address to the right . . . etcetera.

There was a pause. "Holy cat," she said finally, "if I'd known it was anything like this—why, our customers will think we're advertising stationery for lunatics, who don't know who they are."

I turned round from the counter to face her. "Miss Bredin," I said desperately, "that's a quotation from *Alice in Wonderland*. I did the whole page that way. They're all quotations. I've been fighting for them all over the store. But if you think it's terrible, standing up for me the way you did, I'll change the whole thing."

She suddenly put her hand out and squeezed my shoulder hard. "You probably wouldn't know in twenty-five years," she said, "what I know about engraving. Why should I think I know about advertising? If the ninth floor says it's all right, that's good enough for me. Now you go along, and don't pay attention to what *any-body* on the floor says."

I left the section on as close to a run as Marshall Field & Company rules would permit.

The remaining OK's were as easy to get as if the Buyers had really liked what they were signing. They didn't, but the sight of the signatures, "Tracy," "Harris," et alii, brought them into line with only a mumbling of protest.

I walked into Miss Gardner's office, giddy with success, and without even asking in advance if I might see her. I spread the pages on the desk in front of her, and it was a gratifying sight to watch her eyes widen as she checked the OK's.

"I don't know how you ever got them," she said finally, and added, "I think that's something I'd better never know. You must have been either dishonest or immoral. Just don't tell me."

The OK'd pieces were put in a special file after I had made a copy for the printer, the Art Department and one for myself. It was important, Miss Gardner explained, to keep the OK's separate, so they could not possibly be mislaid. Because not infrequently a Buyer going through the magazine at its publication would assert he had come upon merchandise from his section he had never authorized and had certainly not seen before what was written about it. At such moments, an OK'd copy was invaluable.

Miss Gardner gave me a number of pages to do after that; there wasn't anyone else to write them and Miss Gardner had her hands full planning and assembling the over-all and then working with the Art Department. I combined in these pages a conservative tone with a fancy style. I had no difficulties securing OK's.

The head of Millinery particularly liked my caption:

Paris Intrigues in Strawcloth and Milan,

clucked happily over such gems as:

The Orient beguiles the continent, and the rest of us as well, with a deep brown strawcloth turban. Predominantly Egyptian is the brown and tan raffia motif that extends over the entire foreground,

and gave a happy nod to:

All the tangy luxury of sea and air are enfolded in this filmy toque of beige georgette ornamented in blue and silver strands and buttons. Close-fitting hats aplenty of the "airplane" type have come from abroad to delight the traveler.

A double spread on underwear, "Lanjeray" to a Buyer, won rousing approval with the headline:

Some Sources of Feminism and Their Development—A Rather Personal Outline.

Mrs. Ward, the department head, considered it catchy and cute, she said, and

Spring Fashions Take Their Youthful Way

drew a gladsome OK from the Misses' Suits.

This taste of success went straight to my head. I felt a warm affection for Buyers, and confidence that the Buyers loved me. The "Little Things Noticed" page became only a dim memory. I reported nightly to the family my steady progress onward and upward, and accepted complacently, though modestly, their approbation. I brought home a copy of each page as it was OK'd, leaving the original of course locked in the files.

But after reading the first few pages I brought home, mother began to express more enthusiasm for my having got approval of them than for the pages themselves. She finally came round to saying one evening after reading my most recently completed prose gem, she was sorry I didn't have to work a little harder for my OK's. I protested, outraged, that first she had wanted me to have a job and then, when I seemed to be getting on in it better than at first, she complained. She rejoiced every day, she assured me, that I had a job, but she could not honestly rejoice over my writing. It might satisfy the Buyers, but it did not satisfy her. She had liked the "Little Things Noticed" page because I had tried to do something different, and the fact the Buyers were disturbed by it was only proof to her that I had contributed something a little different. That the succeeding pages had had easy endorsement, in her opinion, ought to make me feel disturbed rather than elated.

I started to protest but she requested me sternly to allow her to finish. She knew, she continued, how important it was to earn the friendship and confidence of the Buyers, but easy writing, and, in her judgment, poor, was not the best way to achieve this relationship. If a customer's interest in merchandise was provoked best by flat statistics about it, she could not see the need, she said, of an Advertising Bureau. But if the function of an Advertising Bureau was to write about merchandise, then you ought to write the best you knew how.

We were sitting during this discussion on either side of the fireplace, the page I had brought home on a low table between us. Father was across the room by a reading lamp, enveloped by the evening paper. When mother had finished her demolition, he lowered his paper and looked at me over the top of it. "I wouldn't argue about writing with your mother if I were you," he said, "because you're licked before you start."

"But father," I protested, my voice quivering with indignation, "she's never worked anywhere. She doesn't know how you have to get on with an organization, that's what they keep telling me at the store. She thinks you can do anything you want. You can't."

Mother leaned across the little table between us and patted my knee. "I don't know any of the things you're learning every day," she said, "and that's how it should be. Carve for your children a niche a little higher than the one you live in, 'else wherefore born?' That's what I live by. That's what I believe in, that's why I'm ambitious for you. And you'll be ambitious for your children just the same way. Writing has nothing to do, however, with what I want for you. I'm passionate about writing for itself. I can't let any child of mine slide into a niche of holding a job by virtue of conciliation. If you can't write the best you know how, whatever that is, and then make that best palatable to the other people concerned, then for the love of Heaven, get into some other kind of job."

I picked up my page and went to bed.

The next morning Miss Gardner had another assignment for me, a page on corsets, she said. I would find the merchandise at the pass-out desk. The Corset Buyer had sent it up with accompanying descriptions. Miss Gardner handed me those in an envelope. There was no need, she said, for me to go down to the section to look over the merchandise, because there wasn't much selection to be made among corsets from a standpoint of style or what would illustrate best.

I went around to the pass-out desk, next door to Mr. Exley's office, and opened the boxes there, spreading the contents along a wide table where merchandise was examined, when artists took it out and brought it back. The contents of those boxes made an appalling sight. They were shapeless garments made of heavy rubber. The only differences among them were of color, size and thickness. They were revoltingly slippery to handle and unpleasant to smell.

I took from the envelope the description of these monsters and read they were reducing garments, guaranteed by the sweating induced to melt away pounds. Looking at them, I did not doubt for a moment their guarantee. But the prospect of a page of these illustrated in the magazine would not please anyone, of this I was confident.

I selected one in a strawberry hue and took it to Miss Gardner. She gave a piercing cry at the sight of it. "Never mind," I said soothingly—I'd had a few moments ahead of her to get over my initial shock—"I'll just take them back and explain we can't possibly use merchandise like this in the magazine."

Miss Gardner shook her head. "That's just it," she said mournfully, "you can't. I should never have left the selection of any merchandise to the department. I never dreamed there were such revolting models as these, no matter what they do for you. But I told the Buyer she could send up whatever she wanted. I don't know who else would want it, but this is what she fancies, and I can't throw it back at her. I'll talk to the artist and see if we can't, between us, think up something to do to help their appearance. I don't know what you can say about them, but try your hardest."

I returned the little bijou to the pass-out desk and went to my own, where I read again the descriptions. They were not inspiring. They referred to what I had seen as "a refining girdle," and I did count that a delicate phrase. They further assured the reader that to wear the "refining girdle" faithfully, the length of time not specified, would bring about a change of figure.

I brooded for a long time over what I, in turn, would write. This was not a topic I would have chosen by which to vindicate myself to mother, but I was nettled by what she had said the night before. At least I would not be glib, I promised myself, and wondered how anyone could be glib about "refining girdles."

All morning I wrote down ideas for an approach to the exposition of these objects. Some time around noon I tore them all up. Buff Corse and Peggy Haggett called to me from the gate to have lunch with them. I waved them on, calling I couldn't take the time. Miss Gardner went by with Frances Hooper and to my astonishment stopped at the gate and asked if I would like to join them. This was the first time I had been invited into that circle, but harassed as I was by rubber garments, I felt unequal to the occasion. I told Miss Gardner I was terribly sorry but I had another engagement.

Some time later I went down to the tearoom, got a sandwich, came back and continued writing and tearing up. I couldn't do any actual copy until I had the layout, but I could plan the idea of the general theme, if I had any ideas, and I hadn't. The Art Department made up the layouts.

A layout, I'd learned, was the term for an over-all plan of a page. In the case of *Fashions of the Hour* the layout was done on a special kind of lined paper to indicate type spaces and exactly the size of a *Fashions of the Hour* page. The positions of the illustrations were indicated and, roughly, their basic design. Blocks of type were cut out of old copies of *Fashions of the Hour* and pasted on the layout in exactly the places they would occupy on the final page and in the exact size. Three layouts were made for each page; one kept in the Art Department, the second by the Artist, and the third given as a model to the copywriter. The copywriter receiving it would not only know whether to say the piece of merchandise described was to the left, right, or above, but would also know exactly how many words to write about that piece. It was necessary to count every word in the pasted-up block of type; even more specifically than that, count the number of letters and punctuation marks, making the total of the new copy tally with the model.

Along about the middle of the afternoon Albert brought to my desk my layout for the corset page. The idea for the drawings was surprisingly gay, the rubber monsters were shown on stout ladies dancing into happy, slim figures. I propped the layout in front of me, counted words, space and punctuation for each block of copy and began to write again.

By the end of the afternoon I was not happy with what I had done. I tore it all up.

That night I had little to report to the family, save that I was working on another assignment. I avoided conversation with mother, though I sensed she would not refer to what she had said the night before. I went to bed early and dreamed of "refining girdles."

To make those garments palatable, at least acceptable, took three days of writing and tearing up. At the end of that time I felt I had conscientiously done my best for them, but I still lacked a headline. I was obsessed by rubber corsets, but I could not find words of introduction to them. I sat at my desk; I wandered through the store; I ate lunches alone; took long walks afterward and realized from the startled looks on the faces of passers-by I was muttering to myself.

And then one morning at my desk the title came, clear and complete, so exactly right, it would make everyone happy—and I felt sure of this—everyone from the Buyer, through the ninth floor, to my mother. It was a line from the fifth book of Virgil's *Aeneid* that might have been written for the sole purpose of presenting favorably "refining garments." "Even these things," the line read, "may one day be pleasing to remember." I typed it joyously across the top of the page: *"Haec et forsan meminisse iuvabit."* I whirled it out of the machine, added it to the copy already written, and with the first light step in days took it straight to the Corset Department.

The Buyer was not in, her assistant said, and would allow no one else to OK copy. I assured her that would be entirely satisfactory. I would leave the copy with the assistant to give her. There was nothing in it to warrant my going over it with her.

The rest of the day passed like a happy dream. I went out to lunch with Buff Corse, Peggy Haggett and Eleanor Hunter. In the afternoon I dropped in on Mr. Exley and, later on, my friend Miss Lacey in the Sports Department. I told her as we talked I'd just done a page for the Corset Section and was waiting for an OK. Miss Lacey asked if I knew the Buyer and I said no, I'd not met her. I asked what she looked like. Miss Lacey said she was a fine-looking woman, had red hair and always wore pinned on the front of her dress or blouse the same piece of jewelry, a crown with a cross through it, the whole made of platinum set with diamonds and pearls.

"They say," Miss Lacey added reflectively, "you can always tell when she's mad by the way that pin vibrates. But I don't know if that's true."

We talked for a while longer; Miss Lacey showed me some of the newest things that had just come into the section. It was about five o'clock when I got back to my desk and I was getting ready to go home when I caught sight of a woman coming along the aisle, past the Executive Offices. The first thing I noticed was that she was walking fast with a heavy step; then I saw she had red hair, and suddenly my eye fell on something that seemed to be vibrating so rapidly it was only a shimmering light on the front of her dress.

She passed the Executive Offices and our pen, but brought up at the Advertising Bureau. Albert was at his desk but he could have heard her from mine, because I heard her easily. "Is there a Miss Kimbrough in this department?" she asked.

Albert stood up, looked across at me, and smoothed the back of his hair with his hand. It was a signal, he had told me once, and I remembered it. It meant, "Duck, there's a Buyer after you."

I slid out of my seat and under the desk. Albert raised his voice for my benefit, and told her I was not at the moment in the office. He asked if there was a message, and her answer came across the aisle to me, loud and clear. It probably went all the way into the Household Utilities Department. "Yes," she trumpeted, "you can give Miss Kimbrough a message. You can tell her for me that when I want a caption in Yiddish for my Jewish trade, I'll let her know."

# \* *9* \*

THE FIRST month in the Advertising Bureau I received no pay, though I began thinking about it within a few moments of getting the news I had been hired. By the end of the first week I was like a child at a birthday party waiting for the prizes to be distributed and with much the same feeling of excited uncertainty as to what the prize would be.

At our first interview Miss Gardner had not mentioned pay nor referred to it when she told me over the telephone I had been accepted. During each of these two conversations I had been in a condition closely resembling a trance, and consequently able at best only to acquiesce in what was said to me.

The first week passed without any prize for me. I was only a little dashed by this. The oversight, I conjectured, had something to do with the day on which I had started to work, probably after the books were closed. This was a phrase I had heard somewhere in connection with money and it satisfied me. But only for a week.

When the prize distribution passed me by the second week I looked for another reason. I was embarrassed to take up the matter with Miss Gardner on the premise that it was impertinent for me to discuss anything so personal unless she brought it up first.

I thought of taking up the matter with my new friends in the

Bureau, but came to the decision that would be equally bad manners. What they would think of me I shuddered to imagine, if I were suddenly to talk about how much money they made, or how much I was going to make, and asking when I would get it. They had of course been brought up as I had been, never to discuss money. Since there was no one then to whom I could turn, I worked out a solution for myself. I was, I decided, on two weeks' trial. That was the way servants were hired and fired. It must be true of all employees. This reasoning convinced me so thoroughly that toward the end of the second week I began to pray earnestly that I would not see a pay envelope, because if I did that would mean I had been unsatisfactory and was being let go.

I was radiantly happy, then, when the third week began and no pay envelope had come my way. But when that week had gone all the way by without a prize to me, finding a reason that would satisfy me was difficult. Getting paid by the month was the best I could do, though I had frequent pangs of uncertainty over that reasoning. I had heard the girls talk about a chronic end-of-the-week financial strain. I knew the existence in constant circulation of the rolling dollar in the Bureau. I could only adjust these factors to a monthly pay check by surmising that the girls were on a weekly self-imposed budgeting. But as I came every day to know these girls better, the possibility of such practical economics on their part faded.

Although no mention of it was made at the store, the matter was delicately introduced at home, and that only increased my discomfort. I brought it on myself by requesting from my father an advance on the following month's allowance. Father granted this but made the observation that though he didn't suppose for a minute Marshall Field & Company was paying me anything much in the way of salary, still he hoped it was enough to cover carfare and incidentals so that my having a job would not be too great a financial drain on him. I assured him loftily that my salary was more than sufficient for such trivia, but because of the store's restrictions to dark blue or black clothes, I'd had to buy new outfits beyond what I had anticipated. Father was reassured by this.

I wished with all my heart I could give myself a parallel reassurance. I had had to buy new clothes. They would take every penny of the allowance advanced to me, and I wouldn't have so much as carfare left.

One night in bed brooding over the financial morass I was in, I sank deeper with a sudden remembrance of characters I'd read about in English novels, principally Dickens, who served apprenticeships of seven years or more without pay. I reasoned, in a desperate effort to regain a footing, that such conditions could not possibly exist any longer. But I couldn't convince myself that the principle might not still be the same, only the period of time lessened. If it were lessened all the way down to six months that would be too long for me. I couldn't ask my father to support me in a job, even for that length of time.

The next day I paid the bill for my clothes, but for three days after that I didn't eat lunch, and I rode to and from work on the bus because it cost less than the Illinois Central train, though it took a little over twice as long. I had just enough money to last through the week.

Friday morning after another almost sleepless night, I had gathered sufficient courage to go to Miss Gardner and announce my resignation. I owed it to her, I had decided, to say frankly that my only reason for leaving what had been one of the most thrilling experiences in my life, was that my father couldn't afford for me to have a job. I had decided, too, to invent some other reason to give my family. I could not humiliate my father by facing him with the true one.

I was inside the Bureau on my way to Miss Gardner's office when Buff Corse hailed me. "Payman's coming," she announced, "looks like the Angel Gabriel to me, bless his heart." I hurried on. "I'll get yours for you," she called after me.

As soon as I was in her office Miss Gardner began talking about some cuts that had come in for a page, and I waited with my news until she should have finished. Buff came in while Miss Gardner was still talking. "Excuse me, Achsah," Buff said to Miss Gardner, "but I don't want Emily to think I've misappropriated her funds." She turned to me, her forehead wrinkled in bewilderment. "Honey, that payboy says he hasn't got an envelope for you. He hasn't got your name down at all. You must be getting paid by some other system. But I haven't got your pay envelope, I swear. He says there isn't any."

Miss Gardner was looking as startled as Buff. My face, the back of my neck and my arms grew as hot as if I'd come suddenly to the edge of a bonfire. I felt as if I had, too—the kind of bonfire Joan of Arc had gone into. "I don't get any pay," I blurted. "At least I haven't had any yet."

Buff and Miss Gardner continued to stare at me. "I decided probably apprentices didn't," I trailed off, apologetically.

Buff and Miss Gardner broke in simultaneously. I made out the reiterated theme of their rondo to be that this was the most outrageous thing either of them had ever encountered, that I was the biggest ninny either of them had ever met, not to have spoken up. Did I have some antediluvian idea that a lady—this in icy tones from Miss Gardner—was above such things as money? Or did I intend to be a modern girl, intelligent enough to know that when you took a professional job you took a professional attitude? You expected to be paid and you saw to it that you were.

By this time I wished I were Joan of Arc and that the end would come soon.

Miss Gardner got to her feet. "Come on," she said briskly.

Buff made way for us and I followed Miss Gardner out of the office. She thumped down the aisle and into the timekeeper's office. "What is the reason," she demanded without any preamble, "that Miss Kimbrough has not been getting her pay? I came in with her myself a month ago and signed her on. I should like an explanation."

The timekeeper looked up blandly. "Miss Kimbrough," he said, "has never punched a time clock. So far as we know in this office, she is not working at Marshall Field & Company."

Miss Gardner looked at me. "You said," I stammered, "at least, that is, I thought you didn't approve of time clocks."

Miss Gardner groaned deeply and turned back to the timekeeper. "I will give my personal voucher," she said, "that Miss Kimbrough has worked here every day and all day. I will present that voucher to Mr. Simpson, if necessary."

The timekeeper told her he hoped she would, because he was planning himself to take up the matter with one of the executives. He wanted definite instructions on how to handle this exemption, on the part of the members of the Advertising Bureau, from the time clock. "I don't think the executives know about it."

There was a pause.

"However," when Miss Gardner didn't speak the timekeeper continued, "if you people could see your way clear to observing the rules of the organization like everybody else, I'll take your word that Miss Kimbrough's been working here, and have her pay check made out. And then there'd be no need of you or me going to the management."

Miss Gardner took a deep breath. I think perhaps she was counting up to ten before answering. "Very well," she said.

We left the office together but she did not speak to me on the way back to the Bureau. I followed her through the gate. She stopped at the doorway where my friends were working at their desks.

"I have news for you," she said, and they all looked up. "In order to get her pay, Miss Kimbrough has put the whole Advertising Bureau back on the time clock. She was being a lady."

## 10

MY PAY turned out to be $35 a week. This was a stunning surprise to me and almost that to Miss Gardner. The amount of my check, which I showed her immediately I had received it, jolted from her the revelation that she had recommended $25 a week, but she added, "I know I write figures very poorly."

My allowance was $75 a month. Four weeks' work brought me $140. It seemed to me that by moving from leisure to labor, I had crossed a financial gap equivalent to the size of the Grand Canyon. The crossing might not have made me so giddy had I taken it more slowly, a week at a time, but from nothing to $140 is a heady flight. Almost instantly after catching my breath from it, I went down to Miss Lacey, pausing only to cash my check at the Credit Bureau on the third floor. I wanted to buy, I told her, the checked flannel dress we were going to run in *Fashions of the Hour.* Ever since Miss Lacey had first shown it to me as a suggestion for *Fashions,* I had wanted that dress for week ends in the country. There was no need to try it on. I had done that the first time she'd shown it to me. I took $30 from my pocketbook. "It's $27.50," I told Miss Lacey as I handed her the $30. I knew the price.

Miss Lacey looked at the $30. "Wait a minute, Ducky Feathers," she said, "I don't need all this. Let me figure your discount and then see what I can do."

If she had suddenly clouted me on the jaw, I could scarcely have been more thunderstruck and the effect was, I imagine, much the same. I felt as if I were swaying on my feet while vistas of wild and limitless purchases all over the store popped in front of my eyes. The dress cost $16.75. I took it with me, babbling my thanks.

There were few departments I didn't visit that day, and very few of those I visited in which I did not make a purchase. At intervals I telephoned the Bureau. I was assured by the Art Department that the layout from which I was to work was not ready, and I was requested to stop pestering. I gave Harry Rodman in the Art Department a fervent promise I would not pester further, and I got his promise in return to sign me out as collecting merchandise throughout the store. This was a valid and accurate description of what I was doing.

When I finally returned to the Bureau with the merchandise I had collected, I could scarcely see over the top of the pile of packages I was carrying. Financially, I was down to the bare lunch-and-carfare ground level again, but sartorially I was in full bud and ready to bloom. And with the guarantee of another dazzling $35 pouring down on me in a week's time, I could continue to go onward and upward.

My neighbors, the girls in the stenographers' pen where I was billeted, were surprised when I arrived with my loot. More than one of them asked me as I came up to the gate if I'd heard that Marshall Field & Company had a delivery system. Another of them surmised, to the delight of the rest, that we were so far ahead on the magazine I must have got to thinking it was time for Christmas shopping. But they helped unload me.

I stacked my packages around me on the floor and on the desk. Albert came across the aisle, "Holy cow," he called from the gate, "are you there, Miss Kimbrough? I can hardly see you for the bundles. Miss Gardner's got news for you."

Miss Gardner's news was that we were going to photograph that night, after the store closed, for *Fashions of the Hour*. She apologized for not having given me more warning, but explained that the merchandise she'd been waiting for had just come in and she'd decided to have it photographed rather than sketched.

"Plates from photographs are tricky," she told me, "so I have to allow extra time in case either they or the photographs have to be remade. Eugene Hutchinson is the photographer we use most. He can give us tonight. I hope it won't upset any plans you've made," she added. "I tried several times earlier to reach you but you've been checked out as collecting merchandise over the store. Are you thinking of changing the merchandise in any of the pages you've done?" she asked anxiously.

I assured her I'd had no such idea in mind. "While I was waiting for a layout," I said, "I was familiarizing myself with different kinds of merchandise." I thought this summed up pretty neatly what I had been doing and Miss Gardner accepted it.

She handed me a list of what would be needed for the photographs and asked me to see that all the items on it were collected in the part of the Antique Section she had selected as a setting for the photographs. I would have to get an OK from the Buyer on the loan of whatever we needed, she instructed, and emphasized that I must make sure each article was properly vouched for and brought to the place by a representative from that section.

She also suggested I stop on my way and get some sandwiches for both of us from the tearoom. She had a list of things to assemble as long as mine. She showed it to me. We could eat, she said, while Mr. Hutchinson was setting up his lights.

I telephoned mother this newest requirement in my career, thinking ruefully as I waited for the connection, of the fashion show I had planned that evening for my family. Mother was interested to hear about the photographing but dismayed at the prospect of my coming home late, alone. She drew from me the promise to take a taxi by threatening to refuse permission to me to stay if I did not give it. I wondered just how mother would set about informing Miss Gardner and the Marshall Field organization they could have my services only under certain conditions, and these she would designate. But knowing mother I had the uneasy feeling she would be able to accomplish this in some way of her own, so I gave in about the taxi.

Collecting the merchandise, I made a further discovery about social distinctions in the store. The section heads were pleasant and co-operative about lending anything I asked for: screen, table, a chair, bowls, vases, china, etcetera. But since it was nearing the closing hour, most of the porters had left. There were porters permanently assigned to each floor for the purpose of shifting and carrying merchandise and display cases. The salesgirls I approached refused to carry, or help carry, any of the things to be used in the photographing. Carrying the pieces would not be a physical burden; they were frank about their reason for refusal. Carrying things would be demeaning. They had not been hired to do porter's work. A stockgirl could do that, they explained, if she were available, but not a saleslady.

When Miss Gardner and I met at the place for the photographs, we made the mutual discovery that each of us had carried there the greater number of items from the lists. Over our sandwiches, we advanced to first names, Achsah and Emily. The interval for sandwiches and getting to first names was brief, and the only time during the five hours when we sat down.

My previous and personal experience with photography had given me the happy and erroneous impression of a brief process. When I had been at the lens, I had simply pressed a box Brownie firmly against my middle, looked down into the little glass window on the top of the camera and if both the hands and feet of my subject were visible there, I'd snapped the shutter. Whenever I had been the subject and a visitor to a photographer's studio,

I had been placed on a chair or a piano stool, told to look this way or that, tilt my head, smile. Half a dozen of these maneuvers and the sitting was over. I had not been introduced to photography for a fashion publication.

Some time within the first three hours of my introduction to it, I decided that this branch of the art was no more akin to the branch I had known than a Gobelin tapestry to a cross-stitched guest towel.

I set a table, under Mr. Hutchinson's direction, and it took one hour for the arrangement on it of a lace runner, two bowls, an ash tray and a cigarette box.

Once, when Mr. Hutchinson had run from the table to the shelter of his black shawl, I turned my back to the camera and whispered to Miss Gardner, "Achsah, is it always like this?"

She understood what I meant and nodded. "Always," she said, "that's why it's really better to do it on the spur of the moment. If you think ahead about a photographing date, you lose the strength to meet it."

A long time later, Mr. Hutchinson was happy about the table setting and said so. I eased myself down on the floor and pushed my back against the side of the chest of drawers that was part of the display in the room where we were photographing. There were also antique chairs and sofas in the display, but each of these was occupied by parts of Mr. Hutchinson's equipment. Achsah had found a hassock that was bare, surprisingly, and had hunched herself down on it.

I was so tired I felt lightheaded. I looked down at my legs stretched out in front of me with a detached interest in the fact that they were visibly trembling. As soon as Mr. Hutchinson snapped the shutter, I would have to stand up, but perhaps in the minute or two I estimated the actual photographing would take I might regain the use of my legs, like Antaeus from contact with the ground.

"Now, Miss Kimbrough," Mr. Hutchinson said, "we're ready for the lights."

I was thinking about my legs and heard him only vaguely. He repeated his observation. I looked at him inquiringly.

"Here," he said impatiently, and thrust toward me a large shaded electric light bulb at the end of a long cord.

I didn't think I would be able to stand up but I was, by turning over and doing a pushup. Achsah tottered to her feet.

"Do you want me to hold the screen?" she asked.

"No," Mr. Hutchinson told her kindly, "there's no need for you to bother. Miss Kimbrough can manage both."

Achsah murmured an apologetic "I'm sorry" at me and folded on the hassock again.

Mr. Hutchinson selected from his scattered paraphernalia a piece of heavy cardboard about two feet square.

"Now then," he directed to me, "I'd like you to get up on that chest of drawers, hold the lamp in one hand—we'll work out just where I want it held in a minute—and then with the other hand, I want you to shield it as I direct, with this piece of cardboard."

A small, inner voice told me with conviction we were not going to do any part of this in a minute. I put a dust sheet from a near-by counter on top of the chest of drawers; a highboy, it was. With Mr. Hutchinson's help I climbed to the top of it.

I am not happy on a stepladder. I care very little about looking down from any height greater than my tiptoes. I fancied even less than that standing on the top of an ancient and none too steady highboy, holding aloft in one hand, as Mr. Hutchinson instructed, a very heavy and hot lamp.

Mr. Hutchinson handed up the sheet of cardboard. It was heavy and unwieldy.

"Now," he ordered, "let me get back to my camera and I'll tell you just what to do."

He did tell me for an hour and a half before he snapped the first picture. Sometimes I held both the lamp and the cardboard

Sometimes I held the lamp and the cardboard above my head.

above my head, sometimes I waved the cardboard in front of the lamp. The only thing I was not allowed to do was to sit down.

For the second picture we evolved a new lighting. This turned out to be accomplished by my lying on the floor on my stomach beneath the table on which the display had been set up so long ago. This final position was not come by easily. I had stood on a chair crouched behind a sofa, swung the lamp like a railroad crossing signal, and standing on the top of a neighboring table, cradled it in my arms.

It was only a little after midnight when Mr. Hutchinson decided he had enough to go on.

"We might get something nice," he confided to Achsah, "out of one of these."

What he had got out of me in the process, I yearned to tell him, was almost total disintegration. But speech was too great an effort.

Achsah said we would leave things as they were; the sections would send for their pieces in the morning. But, she added, we'd better be in the store by eight o'clock to supervise their removal, in order to vouch for no damage while they were in our care.

Mr. Hutchinson was skipping about nimbly, collecting his paraphernalia. He refused our offers of help. He was the only one, he said, who knew how to pack the equipment so that it would all fit in his cases. I was delighted to hear it. His hair, worn artistically long, was in confusion from his excursions beneath, and from under, a black coverall. Other than this, nothing in his appearance suggested he had been engaged in any activity. There were smudges of dirt on Achsah's face, apart from dark circles under her eyes. Her hat was askew and her hair straggled from under it.

As I picked up my pocketbook from a corner of the sofa I caught sight of myself in a mirror above it. My face was not streaked, it was all over grimy. I had known for a long time how dirty my hands were. My hat was at an angle I had never before tried. My hair was peeled back underneath it in a tight knot at the back, instead of the carefully waved rolls at the side and loose bun I generally wore. I had arranged it like this at some time during the night, when for the third or fourth time it had fallen down while I was climbing around the furniture with the light. I had no interest in changing my appearance.

Seeing me looking in the mirror a little startled, Achsah stepped beside me, shuddered at her own appearance and walked away. I followed her. We called a good night to Mr. Hutchinson and he called back gaily he'd be around with the proofs in a few days. I muttered to Achsah I hoped it would be a long time before I saw him again! Though, I added, away from his camera I had found him early in the evening, as I dimly remembered, a delightful and interesting person.

"You'll see a *lot* of him," Achsah answered somberly. "We're going to use a good many photographs in this issue."

We reached the first bank of elevators. Signs posted, one at each end of the line, read, THESE ELEVATORS NOT RUNNING.

We moved to another bank—the same notice. After the third try, Achsah said, "I know there's one car running somewhere, but we might as well walk downstairs as tramp all over the store looking for it. At least I know where the stairs are."

At the head of the stairs, I remembered the packages around my desk, my beautiful purchases of the day, up on the ninth floor, unguarded.

"Go ahead," I said, "I have to go back to the ninth floor."

If I had told her I was not going to bother with the stairs, but jump down, she could scarcely have looked more horrified, and announced vehemently that even to think of such a thing was impossible.

I was equally vehement in my insistence that I had to go and finally persuaded her to leave me; but she promised to see that the watchman at the door would have a taxi waiting for me. She told me which door was kept open all night for late employees, adding grimly she was glad the same door was always used. You didn't have to hunt around for it as you did for elevators.

I climbed the four flights with suddenly renewed strength because I was scared of the silence, the emptiness and the dim light. At my desk it took several tries to arrange the packages so I would be able to see my way down the steps. I didn't try exploring other banks of elevators to find the car that Achsah had said was running. The stairs seemed cosier than the open expanses of the ninth floor; and fatigue, I reasoned, was so well settled in, there was no point in exchanging that for nervousness.

I went down at a pretty good clip, in case there should be something behind me, and was breathless when I reached the door and the night watchman. At the sight of me, though he couldn't have seen much of me around the packages, he called, "I got a taxi for you. I guess you're the lady Miss Gardner said was coming."

I promised him I was and added I didn't think I'd ever been so grateful to anybody for anything.

"That's all right," he told me, but as I started to pass him, and he stepped back to allow for the passage of me and my bundles, he put out his hand.

"Pass-outs," he said.

"What?" I asked.

"Pass-outs," he repeated. "I hope you've got 'em handy. Pity to have to lay down all them bundles."

"I haven't got any," I said. "I don't know what they are."

The watchman looked at me in amazement. "Why, my God, young lady," he said, "excuse me, but do you mean to stand there and tell me you're an employee of this store and you don't know you've got to have a pass-out to take merchandise?"

No, I told him, I didn't know it. "I've only been here a month and this is the first time I've bought anything."

That seemed to surprise him almost as much as my ignorance of pass-outs.

[ 143 ]

"You've been in Field's a month and you haven't bought anything?" he echoed.

"Look," I said urgently, "Miss Gardner identified me. She told you I was coming."

"I know you're an employee," was his answer, "so you've got to have a pass-out. Those are the rules. That's what I'm here for, to see merchandise don't get taken out of the store." Then he relented a little. "Well, maybe," he said slowly, "if they're charged to you and you got an account here, and you can show me the charge slips, maybe this once, being you've worked so late, I'll let you through. But it would cost me my job if anyone was to hear of it."

"I have an account," was my answer, "but I didn't charge any of these things. I paid for them."

"Well," he said briskly, "I guess that settles it then. They'll have to stay here."

"All right," I told him resignedly, "but take care of them, will you, please? They're awfully important."

His eyes widened again with surprise. "Me take care of them?" he said, "why, you must be a little 'touched.' I couldn't take the responsibility. You'll just have to put 'em back where you got 'em from."

"On the ninth floor?" I asked, and my voice sounded to me like the tremolo stop on an organ.

"I can't help where it is," he answered stolidly. "You certainly can't leave 'em laying around."

I would have been glad to lay them around anywhere and lay me down to sleep on top of them. I made that suggestion but the watchman would have none of it.

"Well," I finally put it to him, "can you at least tell me which elevator is running?"

"Funny you should ask me that," was his answer.

It was in my opinion as unfunny a question as I had ever posed.

"I always make it a point to find out which shift is running, every night when I come on, but just tonight I had something else on my mind, and I clean forgot."

I climbed the nine flights of stairs, put my packages on and around the desk and came down again to the watchman. As I approached him, I watched with interest the way the floor seemed to be moving in waves and I had to climb over them.

The watchman called, "Everything all set now, I guess. I got your taxi still waiting for you."

"Thank you so much," I told him, and left the store.

As I climbed in the cab, I looked at the big Marshall Field clock hanging out over the corner on State and Washington Streets. It said twenty-five minutes to two. The taxi meter read $1.25. When I gave the driver my address I asked him how much he thought it would cost to get there.

"Around $2.50," he said.

I had $1.50 in my pocketbook, and I didn't in the least care.

About fifteen minutes on our way I was overwhelmed by a sudden rise of nausea, and I whiled away the rest of the trip by throwing up out the window.

I was quite right not to have worried about not paying the taxi fare. When we drew up in front of my address, I saw all the lights on in our apartment. After I had closed the door of the taxi, I looked up again. Mother was standing at one window, father at another. I waved to them. They were ready to open fire when father opened the door for me, but one look convinced them I had not been out on the town. They swerved their attack instantly from me to Marshall Field & Company. And the last plan I heard, after father had paid the taxi and mother had helped me undress, put me into bed and given me a glass of hot milk to drink, was father's announcement that he would write personally to Mr. Simpson.

The atmosphere cleared rapidly at breakfast the next morning when, after admitting the weeks I had gone without salary but had been afraid to say anything about it, I'd given quickly the follow-up announcement that I'd received the preceding day a check for four weeks' work, amounting to $140. But at my further tidings of purchases made the day before, though I did not enumerate them, father lapsed into gloom again. Mother volunteered, however, to drive me downtown in the Electric to make sure I would be there by eight o'clock, in order not to jeopardize my job since I was doing so well.

That week end I spent in Lake Forest. I told my friends there about my night of photographing and repeated what Achsah had said at some time during those long hours.

"One day," she had prophesied, "you'll watch someone leaf through an issue of *Fashions of the Hour* and come on the page of photographs from this night's work. The most that you can hope for is that that person will pause for a moment before turning the page."

My friends commented things like, "Heavens, then why do you make such a bother about them?"

The audience that during the earlier week ends had been spellbound by stories about my job was getting bored by them. I told other anecdotes. I described people I was meeting in the store, friends I was making there. My listeners became noticeably restive. I suggested we all get together at a lunch I would give in the tearoom of my own store. And after lunch I would take my pals from the country on a tour of the store, show them parts of it I was sure they'd never seen before, introduce them to some Buyers.

As I outlined it on the spur of the moment, my plan for this social gathering grew more dazzling to my own vision, but provoked only polite and evasive responses from my listeners. They were preoccupied, I learned, when my own babbling ran down, with a dinner dance the family of one of our group had been cajoled into giving for her. The dance was to take place, my gang told me breathlessly, about two months from this Saturday on which we were talking about it.

[ 146 ]

During the rest of that week end whenever I mentioned the store, or at almost any other time, people told me about the party; how big it was going to be, what orchestra was going to play, and what the decorations would be. I was excited to hear about it, but I was preoccupied, too, with matters concerning the magazine; sketches about which Achsah and I had not on Friday been entirely happy, an artist who was being held up because merchandise had not arrived—she might not wait for it but take up another job and then whom would we get? The mother of one of my friends in the Bureau might have to have an operation, and how on earth would my friend pay for it?—she supported her mother. Peggy Haggett's love affair was going badly, and one of my Buyer friends had had an offer of a job in New York, but was afraid there was a catch in it somewhere, and also hated to leave Field's, though the pay would be much higher. She would have to give her answer Monday.

Listening to the talk around me, I found it hard to get my mind off the people at the store; I was with them all day, every day in the week until Sunday. My life, I ruminated, seemed to have become more bound up with theirs than with these friends in Lake Forest, of much longer standing; but I only saw the Lake Forest group on Sunday now, and not every Sunday.

Next week end I was too tired by Saturday afternoon to go out to the country, and telephoned I couldn't come. We'd been working hard every day and late on several nights. The night sessions hadn't been quite so bad as the first one, partly because I was prepared for them, and partly because we'd ascertained ahead of time what elevator would be running.

Gathering merchandise one afternoon the following week for a night photographing bout, I saw in the Misses Section a party dress that I tagged instantly as the essence of everything that was beautiful in every party dress I'd seen all my life. At the same instant, I remembered the dinner dance that was going to take place. If I wore that dress I would be a success—I had no doubt about it—the kind of success that would lead man after man to cut in on me before I had danced three yards, and every girl friend, acquaintance or total stranger look at me with longing tinged with loathing.

The dress was the color of champagne, made of tulle, with bunches of red velvet cherries on green leaves, appliquéd on the full skirt. To my amazement I saw it had a reduced tag on it. Why it had not been sold the moment it had been placed on the floor, I couldn't imagine. From $150 to $100, I read. I hunted up the Buyer who was a friend, and asked her about it.

"Honey," she said, "I don't know what I can do for you. That's a big reduction, as you can see. I don't know why the dress didn't sell. I think it's one of the prettiest we've ever shown, but," and she shrugged her shoulders, "you can never tell." She looked at it a minute. "If it doesn't sell this week, I'll take it down a little, and you can have it."

I begged her to keep it hidden as much as she could on the rack so no customer could see it. She promised she would, but warned me she couldn't take it off sales.

The rest of the day, gathering merchandise for the photographs, I brooded somberly on my feckless spending of the first salary check. Now I couldn't buy a hundred-dollar dress, and the Lord only knew, I told myself, when there would be another party on such a scale as the one ahead.

I went every day to see the dress, almost afraid to look on the rack lest it should have gone. And every day when I found it, I waited until the salesladies were momentarily out of sight, then pulled other dresses around and over it to keep my treasure hidden.

The following Monday morning I was in the section on the dot of eight-thirty. The dress was there too. The Buyer didn't come in until nearly ten o'clock. She'd left word in the section she was going first to see a local manufacturer, and didn't know what time she'd get into the store. If she hadn't got in until

[ 148 ]

closing time, I would have waited, no matter how much I might be needed at my own job. I sat on a chair in the section with the dress over my arm. The Buyer had promised that on Monday morning she would take it off sale. I was doing it for her.

When she came in finally, I told her I just happened to be passing through the section and also just happened to know where the dress was, so I had thought to save her the bother of getting it for me. She said she really oughtn't to take it off sale yet—my heart sank—but if I were sure I could use it. . . .

I told her I had never been surer of anything. . . .

And there wouldn't be any question of returning it . . . ?

I promised that nothing in the world would tempt me ever to return that dress.

Very well then, she'd let me have it for $85.

I bought it, and I went back to the ninth floor, the box in my arms, my heart bursting with love for Buyers and for Marshall Field's. As soon as I got home that evening I put it on for my parents. Mother was gratifyingly enthusiastic; father gave a long whistle of approbation, very satisfying.

I hung it away carefully, a sheet wrapped around it.

The pace of the magazine was mounting. We were coming near the date set for going to press. Merchandise came to the checking counter in the Bureau, and went out on the gallop to artists. Artists came back on the run with sketches. I went with the artists to get OK's from the Buyers in case there should be any difficulty, and there frequently was. Finished drawings went to the engravers, plates came back, were returned for sharpening, clearing, sometimes redoing. The standard for *Fashions of the Hour* was high. I wrote copy to the pasted-up layouts, rewrote it, took it home, worked on it at night, finally submitted it to Achsah, and, after her approval, to the Buyers. Page proofs came from the printer's to be read meticulously for accuracy, and then reread by Mr. Exley.

[ 149 ]

For the second Sunday I did not go out to Lake Forest. I worked all day.

The following week the pressure was, if anything, greater. Last-minute corrections, substitutions of merchandise when it was unexpectedly discovered a manufacturer would not be able to supply the estimated quantity required for orders from the magazine.

For the third Sunday I didn't go out to my friends in Lake Forest.

The following week the magazine went to press. Achsah, the Art Director and I accompanied it to the printer's, one evening about eight o'clock. We had eaten dinner together around six, and worked again in Achsah's office until the telephone call came that the pages were ready. The printers were the Reuben H. Donnelley Corporation, and Mr. Reuben Donnelley was the father of Eleanor, one of my oldest friends and my roommate at college. The last time I'd been in Lake Forest I'd stayed at her house, and when my friends had not been interested in stories about Field's I was bursting to tell, Mr. Donnelley had taken me into his library and we'd had a long talk there. He'd been interested and had told me in turn a great many things about the Donnelley Corporation and about printing. We had talked two hours or more and had come in together Monday morning on the early train. When we'd separated at the station he had said, "Maybe I'll see you one day at our plant, Emily."

And when Achsah, the Art Director and I came into the big building of Reuben H. Donnelley Corporation to put *Fashions of the Hour* on the press, the doorman asked, "Is one of you ladies Miss Kimbrough?"

I identified myself.

"Mr. Reuben Donnelley told me to let him know when you came in. He's waiting in his office; he wants to see you."

A gentleman stepped out from a little room near the entrance, introduced himself and said he'd been delegated to take us to the office where we would read final proofs, and to see that we were comfortable. He would also let Mr. Donnelley know when we were installed.

The room in which we were placed had a long, broad table with overhead lights of an unearthly bluish-green color; the same color, I observed to Achsah, that the machine in our garage gave off when our Electric automobile was being charged from it. Page proofs were spread about on the broad table, and our guide indicated a large supply of pencils close at hand for each of us.

Achsah said she hoped we were not inconveniencing anyone by this invasion. It was the first time a *Fashions of the Hour* staff had moved bodily to the printer's, she explained to me. The reason for it was that we could cut off several days from our schedule, she hoped, by checking each proof as it was pulled, and, in the event of corrections, see a revised one. When messengers had to go back and forth between Donnelley's and the store, hours, even days, were lost. We wanted, she said, by the end of the evening to see every page with its final OK into the lockup, adding in an aside to me, that when a proof went into the lockup that was the end of it, except in the case of the direst emergency.

Our guide approved the plan, he said, though he added, confidentially, the printers themselves were some of them dubious about women being around the plant.

The Art Director spoke up. "I'm offering," she said, "a box of cigars apiece to the typesetters and the engravers, if the book is in the lockup tonight."

The gentleman in attendance on us beamed at this and said he would relay the message immediately; it would make a great difference.

Somebody called out, "Hello there," and I turned around from the table to see Mr. Donnelley coming toward us, and, to my utter astonishment, my father behind him. When I had introduced them both to Achsah and the Art Director, father explained he had no intention of allowing me to come home in the early morning. He'd sensed from my description at breakfast of the program, that it had the earmarks of an all-night session. He'd called Mr. Donnelley to find out where in all probability we would be located, and learned, to his pleased surprise, that Mr. Donnelley himself intended staying to see us on our way. The two men had dined together, but Mr. Donnelley was planning to catch within a short time the train for Lake Forest. Father would stay on.

I tried every argument to induce father to leave with Mr. Donnelley, because I was humiliated that a professional woman should have her father sitting around while she did her job. Father was adamant, however, and mildly suggested I save my breath.

Mr. Donnelley welcomed another gentleman who came up to the table and introduced him to us. It was Mr. Kittredge, he said, who probably knew more about printing than anybody in the world. Mr. Kittredge modestly disclaimed this, but assured us he'd be glad to help on any matters of type.

Mr. Donnelley left soon after. He'd been so interested, he said, he'd have to hustle to make the train. We three from *Fashions of the Hour* took our pencils and began to work on the pages waiting for us. My father settled himself in a corner under the blue-green light, and opened up the evening newspaper. Sometime around midnight, he disappeared and came back with sandwiches and coffee for all of us.

That was the only interruption. Typesetters came and went, we conferred over pages and sent them back for alteration, the Art Director working with slide rules, magnifying glass and fine pointed pens. A block of copy came off the press with a hangover, or, as they unattractively phrased it, "bleeding." I'd change the wording no farther back than the preceding line so there would be not too much resetting, and yet achieve a block of copy exactly filled in, no overrun. Achsah checked and rechecked with the original OK'd sheets from the Buyers, brought from the files to this proving ground, and carefully guarded.

It was nearly three in the morning when we had finished, but every page was in the lockup. The magazine was on the press.

Father got a taxi for us with some difficulty. We dropped the Art Director at the station to catch a train, took Achsah to her apartment on the North Side and got to ours around four o'clock.

Our arrival did not waken mother. We were very careful not to let it. I didn't want to answer questions about the printing business, I whispered to father as I gently closed the front door. He whispered back his agreement, and outside his bedroom door added softly, "I had a good time tonight. Do you still like your job?"

I nodded vigorously. "Better than anything I ever did," I hissed, and went on down the hall to my room.

A few days later, Eleanor Donnelley telephoned me. She was in town, she said, and would I lunch with her at Field's? I joined her in the Narcissus Room at one o'clock. She'd heard from her father, she told me, about my night at the printer's. I'd been mortified, I said, at his being there, and more still by the presence of my father; but, I added, I didn't know what you could do about parents. She agreed they were a problem and went on to ask if I was still as crazy about my job as I had been. She hadn't, she said, had a chance to check up with me the last few weeks. I told her I was sorry I hadn't been out to the country, but we'd been busy. I assured her I was crazy about the job, and liked too, I didn't mind saying, getting a salary; furthermore, getting a price on things I bought at Field's. That reminded me of my dress for the party. I described it to her in detail, and when I had finished asked, "By the way, what's the exact date?"

She didn't answer for a minute. Then she looked at me squarely. "It's two weeks from Saturday. The invitations came out last week."

I didn't say anything; I couldn't think of anything to say.

[ 153 ]

Eleanor was the first to speak, and her words came in a rush. "I feel perfectly awful about it, and I'm furious at Amy." Amy was giving the party. "But Amy said her family was wild at the sight of the list and absolutely forced her to cut it down. Amy cut you out because she decided you'd got so wrapped up in your job, you didn't come out any more, you'd sort of lost interest in your old friends, and probably wouldn't care about coming to the party anyhow."

"That's all right," I told Eleanor. "We *are* terribly busy. I probably wouldn't have been able to come."

Eleanor's answer was, "It makes me sick," and added, "Will you promise to come out to me the first Sunday you can get away?"

I said I would, but I knew we both realized it wouldn't be very comfortable for me to see any of those people for a long time after the party, at least until they'd stopped talking about it.

When we finished lunch I asked Eleanor if she'd like to come up and see my office. She said she'd love to another day but she was awfully busy. She was uncomfortable with me, I knew, just as I was with her. I thought it considerate of her not to want to prolong the visit. We said good-by at the elevator; she asked me again to come out as soon as I could, and I said I'd let her know.

I went up to the ninth floor and sat down at my desk, thinking how nice it had been of the Buyer in the Misses Section to take the dress off sale and let me have it, and thinking about my promise to her that I couldn't imagine ever wanting to return it.

## 11

BY THE time we had finished planning the next issue of *Fashions of the Hour*, I had met every Buyer in the store except the Czarina of the Book Section, Marcella Hahner, and those who were abroad on buying trips. I was still wary and in awe of the department heads; others had promoted me to the status of a working friend. Mrs. Hanley in charge of Children's Clothes, who at my first interview with her had likened my coming to the presence of diphtheria in a baby carriage, was now cozy and confidential. But one line of demarcation remained very strong.

Socially, I did not belong in their group. I was never invited to lunch with them, I never saw them outside the store, but during working hours I was their chum. They told me about their home life, their love life and their business worries, and though I never met a friend nor a relative of any of them, nearly every morning on my way to the ninth floor I would stop off at a section to learn from its Buyer what had happened overnight to the particular relative or "fellow" about whom we were at the moment concerned.

I heard, too, about merchandising, aspects of it that had never before occurred to me. Certainly I had not known that every Buyer had on his desk, like an inexorable though silent metronome, a record of the sales total on the corresponding day of the previous year, and readily accessible, both to him and to the management, a record of sales totals on each day of years before that. Therefore, he was under a strain to equal, or beat if possible, that day of the year before, and the years before that.

Almost without exception, every department head I knew carried a small notebook, in which he kept a diary. It was an unusual form of diary, because it included no personal news, but covered any events that affected his sales—the weather and the temperature from eight to ten in the morning, because that is the time when a woman makes up her mind about going shopping. At such and such an hour on such and such a day, the elevated or the Illinois Central train had broken down. Another day's notation would be of a parade that had held up traffic in the Loop and so held back sales. Or, on the other side of the ledger, some particular display of merchandise had stimulated "impulse buying"; a big convention had been held and brought from out of town a buying crowd of women, wives of delegates. That would make a bonanza week, with management up on the ninth floor beaming at sight of the daily sales sheet, some of the executives even coming down to the section to watch the rush and congratulate the Buyer on a selection of merchandise that was moving so fast.

But you paid for it the following year, the Buyers told me, because you were supposed to top the bonanza. By that time the management on the ninth floor had forgotten about the convention, and weren't interested in explanations. They just looked at figures. So, knowing you had that kind of a week coming up, you went to the Advertising Bureau to beg for a little extra newspaper space and an additional cut or two, "cut" meaning a drawing. And generally you were told you had already used the little extra emergency fund over your monthly advertising appropriation, because you'd had previously another big day to beat.

It was no wonder, I realized when I'd heard a few of these

things, the people in the Advertising Bureau were entrenched behind a door with a lock that could open only from the inside. But I wondered that even with that protection the Bureau had not been torn apart at least once by a distraught Buyer with a day to beat and an advertising appropriation exceeded.

I found it remarkable, coming to think of it, that I too had not been torn apart, coming with a humorous ad to be OK'd by a Buyer who had days to beat. Achsah had rocked my equilibrium with the information that Marshall Field & Company spent $250,000 a year on *Fashions of the Hour*, this sum not including my $35 a week and the salaries of the other members of the staff.

But I had supposed, until the Buyers had allowed me to share their sorrows, that the benevolent executives of Marshall Field & Company paid this and the cost of all the other advertising, and looked upon *Fashions of the Hour* indulgently as a luxury, an experiment in prestige advertising, that must never be expected to pay for itself. I was right about their feeling toward the magazine, but profoundly mistaken about their bearing the brunt of the luxury. The sections paid the brunt.

The more Buyers I came to know, and the chummier we became, the more strongly, along with my sympathy, my impression grew to conviction that part of a Buyer's equipment, if not one of his talents, is a misanthropic point of view. He believes, with all his heart, that he is a prey of manufacturers at home and abroad, all store executives, the Advertising Department, and demented individuals who make up the bulk of his customers. The few of these who are not demented are women of such sensitive discrimination, and such exquisite taste, they will buy only from his department when in need of the kind of merchandise he carries, and preferably only from his personal selling.

A search for some kindly light in this encircling gloom prompted me to ask about annual bonuses. These, it was reluctantly admitted, were paid not according to the sales of the individual departments but on a percentage of the store business.

A few of my Buyer chums were unable to see any good even in this, but most of them spoke up in praise. When I myself did not at once see a benefit from the system, the head of the Games Section, to whom I happened to be talking when I first heard of bonuses, explained that a section might drop suddenly in sales and over a considerable period through no fault in merchandising. Instead of being penalized, that section would be carried and receive its quota of over-all bonus. And when it was back on its feet again perhaps another department would be on the downgrade.

Still a little confused, I asked how this skidding came about.

"Why," he said, "take my department right now—Games. We're in the middle of a mah-jongg craze. I never saw anything like it. I can't keep enough sets in stock, and I've bought them by the thousands. I even made a fast trip to China to bring back some beauties, hand-carved, old. I had to charge a price for them that made my own hair curl. They sold like a sale of shower caps on the Notions Counter. I haven't had to use any push money either."

That word was in my notebook of store vocabulary. "Push money" is the extra commission to a clerk who gets rid of merchandise that has not gone well. A salesgirl can add considerably to her earnings in this way, and yet the Buyer does not have to take a loss on the individual articles comparable to the loss this would incur by a big markdown in the selling price.

"And we're not the only ones coming in on this boom," he continued. "The Optical Department is advertising special lenses for seeing the tiles better. And the Lace and Embroidery Department has got a boom on of lace cuffs you pull on over your sleeves in order not to knock over the Wall of China. We've got mah-jongg teachers set up, and they've got every hour taken from eight-thirty in the morning."

He paused, and I ventured to observe as a member of the Advertising Bureau I did happen to know something of the mah-jongg furore and its ramifications.

"Well," he interrupted, "did you know this?" and paused dramatically. "Did you know that I could go home of a Saturday night—and this is probably just what's going to happen—I could go home with a week behind me of the biggest sales we've ever done; come down to work on Monday morning and find the whole mah-jongg craze over. That's the way things can happen in merchandising. You might as well have water-damaged stock from a fire for all your customers will buy it. Somebody, I don't know who, but somebody says, 'I don't think I'll play mah-jongg any more. I'm tired of it, let's play something else,' and boom—it's all over, everybody's tired of it.

"I'm more than tired. I'm sick with the merchandise I've got left on my hands, and I won't be able to give it away across the counter with a box of Crackerjack. But I don't dare let my stock run down. I can't be like that old storekeeper in Maine they tell about, the one who said he wasn't going to stock calico any more because as fast as he got it in it went right out. I've got to keep up the store tradition that 'You can get it at Field's.'"

I began to understand and interrupted him. "That's where the benefit from the bonus system comes in."

He nodded his head several times. "You've hit it," he said. "Now when my inventory is way up and I'm not doing enough business to keep a boy in marbles, I get my annual bonus just the same, based on the store's over-all."

"That's what's been carrying the Veiling Department and the Lace Section. Why, they've got laces down there at a thousand dollars a yard. Probably sell it too, one of these days, for a bride's veil. But their daily turnover makes a mighty small sales sheet. Time was when everything a woman wore from the skin out was trimmed with lace or embroidery, or both. Nowadays you scarcely see it. Just like mah-jongg. One Saturday some stylish woman said, 'I'm tired of lace, I guess I won't wear it any more.' And on a Monday there wasn't any lace business.

"Same thing in Veils. Time was a woman didn't think she was

[ 159 ]

well-dressed if she didn't have a veil over her face. Nowadays, they tell me in that section, they only sell to a few old ladies. But the store carries them. They get their bonus. And some day, lace and veils will be in again. Same thing with Philippine underwear. They're looking for it to drop out any day and customers wanting nothing but silk.

"Household Utilities"—he was naming them off on his fingers—"they had a terrible time 1916 to 1918. Couldn't get the stuff because of the war industries. Of course all our imports suffered then. And people didn't entertain the way they had before. Didn't think it was right."

"Right now we've got a boom on in the Glass Section on account of Prohibition. More people are buying cocktail sets than ever thought of having drinks in their homes before."

"Do they sell a lot?" I asked, surprised. "I understood we're not allowed to advertise them."

My friend chuckled. "You don't advertise them," he said, "that's a store policy. But they're selling them down there all right. And calling them beverage sets. They even get into the Monday advertising sometimes, if you've noticed."

I was proud of knowing what this meant. It was down in my notebook along with the store vocabulary.

By some obscure impulse, the Carriage Trade does its shopping on Monday. Surveys had been made, I'd been told, to track down the basis for this, but were unsuccessful. It was not a Chicago idiosyncrasy, it was a national custom. Buyers from Field's had compared notes in New York with Buyers from all over the country. In cities that boasted a symphony orchestra, fashionable women coming downtown for a Friday concert habitually built their day around that occasion, making it include shopping in the morning and lunch with a friend. But the shopping was desultory. No departments benefited from it except, possibly, the Household Utilities. And that was understandable. Entertaining is generally done during the week end. A prospective hostess—

and she represents a group considerably larger than the concert-goers—contemplating a dinner party on Saturday night, becomes aware on Friday of the lack of a proper roasting pan or some other kitchen utensil, and visits the Housewares. Requests for immediate delivery from that section were always particularly urgent on Fridays.

But the basis for Monday shopping could not be defined. It

was only a long proven fact that Monday shopping was style shopping by the Carriage Trade, and principally for clothes. Therefore, Monday advertising was devoted to style and expensive merchandise. Unless it was an unusual event, no sales were mentioned on that day.

On Saturday the basement had more advertising coverage than any part of the store because that day brought the working girls, and they for the most part headed for the bargains.

On Sunday's Field's ran no advertising; even the curtains were drawn on every show window. The voice of the store grew faint at the end of the week, finally died away all together on Sunday, and then burst into elegant prose and cuts on Monday morning.

Prices too, in that day's advertising if quoted at all, would either be in round numbers or multiples of five. Merchandise was not allowed at any time to be priced on other than a five-cent basis. Marshall Field's held no traffic with 98¢, no matter how many dollars went with it. And in style merchandise, the management disapproved of any number closer to tens than a seven. For example, a dress could be $87.50, but not $88.75. Such price tags, store policy held unworthy of Marshall Field & Company.

Jean Schureman, my friend on the second floor, was the one who had told me about price rules. He was assistant to the Buyer of China, and I went to see him shortly after my visit with the head of the Games Section. I was on another round of "Little Things Noticed." This time it gave me a wonderful opportunity to gossip with the people who were by now my friends. I told Jean about the mah-jongg situation. I was so concerned about it, I said, that every morning when I woke up I wondered if mah-jongg were all over, and I found myself urging my friends outside the store not to get tired of mah-jongg, reproaching them with the information that in China the game had been played for hundreds of years without anyone's growing tired of it. This solicitude on my part had occasionally been bewildering to my friends, I'd discovered, particularly to those who had not yet taken up the game.

Jean's answer to my expressed anxiety was a derisive and coarse laugh. "Tell the fellow in Games," he suggested, "to come down here if he wants to see merchandise that's stuck on the shelves. That's what a China Section is built on. However," he conceded, "I suppose there is a difference. I don't imagine eating off china is going to go out of style, at least not over a week end."

I asked about china merchandising. I liked collecting this kind of information along with the knickknacks for the "Little Things Noticed on a Walk through the Store" page. Jean loved to talk about the store and the people in it. I never heard him malicious, he only expressed his enjoyment of them. At this session when we were talking about merchandise, he suddenly thought of someone he would like me to enjoy, he said.

We were standing as we talked behind a sheltering display table piled with china. He seized my arm and hustled me into the open section. "Come on," he said, "if we can catch Louise Lang, I want you to meet her. She's wonderful and she knows more about this section than all the people in it put together."

As we went up and down the aisles looking for her, Jean gave me an idea of what to expect.

"She's got blonde hair," he said, "maybe with gray in it. It's hard to tell with blondes. Anyway, there's a lot of it and it's in a big pile," he hesitated a minute, "maybe on the top of her head, maybe not. It's always slipping from one side to the other. There's a young Polish girl at the cash desk who does it over for Louise whenever they both have free time. Probably the only thing in the world Louise has to ask someone else to do for her, except her banking," he added.

I saw her ahead of us and recognized her instantly. A large flat coil of light hair hung unsteadily over her left ear. I indicated her to Jean. She was talking to a customer so we didn't move on toward her. While we waited for the customer to finish, I asked Jean how he happened to couple a banker with the Polish girl at the cash desk.

"Because," Jean said, "there's a banker in town who takes care of Louise's money the way the Polish girl watches out for her hair. When he was a cashier he handled Louise's savings account and she began asking his advice about investments. She won't go to anybody else and he takes care of her pennies as if they were thousands of dollars. And I'll bet he always will.*

"She's going to make thousands out of those pennies, too," Jean

* When that banker became the bank's Executive Vice-President, he still came to work half an hour early on the first Monday of every month to meet Louise Lang and counsel with her on her investments. He made this change in his schedule so that she would not lose time in the store. When she died she left $100,000.

continued. "I don't believe she's ever eaten a meal in this store sitting down. She brings a sandwich and barely snatches time to munch that. She won't listen to any rules about an hour out for lunch. She says her time is her own and nobody else is going to tell her what to do with it. Her idea is to make it pay." He chuckled. "She's awfully bucked up lately because she's got Field's helping her save money. She found out the Company buys bulk tickets on trolleys for our repair workmen who do a lot of traveling. Once she got onto that she never let up until she persuaded the Company to get them for her. Her transportation now costs her nine cents a week less than it did before. I bet she takes it over to her banker to keep for her."

I asked if she ever did anything outside of the store.

"I got her to take a bus trip East last summer," Jean said. "It took everybody in the section to help persuade her. She finally gave in on condition she could sit up front next to the driver so as not to miss anything. Of course there are no reserved seats on a bus, but I fixed it for her somehow. The trip included a plane ride at Worcester, Massachusetts, in an open cockpit model. She was the only one of the party who took it. But she made the busload wait for her."

"Did she enjoy the ride?" I asked, "and how did she feel about the whole tour?"

"Well," Jean answered, "she wasn't too enthusiastic when I asked her. She just said, 'It was all right, but don't forget it cost me ninety dollars.'

"Lord, Emily," he burst out, "how she can sell! The number of her customers would pretty nearly populate a small town, and over half of them trust her so much, they just write in or telephone to her to pick out a wedding present for fifty or one hundred dollars or whatever, and send it with the usual message enclosed. They don't even bother to see it.

"One of her customers, an old lady, one of the richest women in Chicago, has Louise spend Christmas with her. She's one of the few of the old guard that still lives on the South Side. All the rest of her family, children, grandchildren, live clear out in Lake Forest. The old lady doesn't like to go out there. So every Christmas Eve she sends her car and chauffeur to the store to pick up Louise. It's the only day in the year Louise leaves early. She cuts off thirty minutes and goes at five. Each of them makes a present by hand, for the other. Louise is taken back home on Christmas night.

"She's free now," he interrupted himself rapidly, "let's catch her quick."

"Jean's been telling me about you," Miss Lang said when we had been introduced. "He says you like to hear about the store."

I assured her I did and added we'd been talking about turn-over in merchandise and merchandise that stayed on the shelves.

"Well," she said, "you've come to the right department for merchandise on the shelves. That's what a China Section is built on, big stock. We were the first to have matching services. Other stores wouldn't give them space, but would refer a customer to us when she asked for additions or replacements. Those customers stayed.

"You know," she began to reminisce, "in the late nineties and early 1900's fine china was all the rage. Women collected it the way people collect pictures, and they talked about it. Why, there was a saying that a wedding wasn't legal unless the bride had a full set of Haviland china. And a full set then, of course, was one hundred pieces."

I said I'd understood Field's had one of the finest collections of Wedgwood in the country.

"In the world," Miss Lang corrected me. "And I can tell you how we got it, too. There was a society woman from Chicago who went to see the Wedgwood Museum when she was visiting in England one summer. She discovered, not in the exhibit but just lying around, some ordinary cream-colored earthenware plates with an embossed vine and figure pattern. This lady had got tired of very ornate china and she liked this. (A descendent of this lady, I thought, is the one who's going to get tired of mah-jongg.) She told Wedgwood she wanted to order a whole set. The Wedgwood people were astonished. They'd produced it as a kind of experiment but had thought nothing of it.

"We didn't know any of this at Field's, of course. But our society customers suddenly began asking for an old Wedgwood set like Mrs. P's. We couldn't figure out what it was, and we knew Mrs. P. would squelch us if we asked her outright.

"On two trips our Buyer made to England he nosed around old antique shops trying to track it down. We had a pretty accurate description of it. He couldn't find it anywhere.

"Then a young member of the Wedgwood family was sent to America to act as agent, and he set up a practice of selling us his samples at half price. One day in New York our Buyer was getting these samples and young Wedgwood suddenly pointed to two dirty plates and said, 'You can have those for ten cents apiece, but you can't sell them. We don't think anything of it, but there's a Mrs. P. in Chicago who's ordered a whole set.' Our Buyer snatched those plates, you can bet. He had the secret then. And as soon as he got back to Chicago he called several of the women who had been asking about this china and told them Field's was now able to supply it. We took orders about as fast as you could write them down. Those women ordered from three to five hundred pieces each.

"Well, the very next week young Wedgwood came to Chicago. And we told him we would order three thousand pounds of this pattern. He nearly fell over, and of course he didn't dare turn down an order as big as that even to keep Mrs. P. exclusive. He said they'd fill it. But we'd thought up a string to attach. We told him we'd only give him the order if the Wedgwood factory would loan us an exhibit from their Museum to show in the store. Young Wedgwood got permission by cable from his father. And our Buyer went right over to England to arrange for the exhibit. The rest of the Wedgwood directors were hopping mad. They didn't want to risk their precious pieces. There was finally a showdown and they gave in. Our Buyer even went so far as to persuade them to make up special pieces to show their skill was still as good as it always had been.

"We put on the exhibit and it was the biggest china show that had ever been held. The society people came in droves, and they ordered like that too. We made a whale of a lot out of it. But the Wedgwood family did even better. The volume business we sent them as a result of that exhibition made a fortune for them. That broke down the opposition of the old British companies to us as a department store. They were delighted to be represented. But the bigger our department grew, and the more firms we represented, the more merchandise we had to keep on our shelves. China factories won't store it, they ship it immediately; it's too expensive to warehouse. There's about a million dollars' worth of china on these shelves right now."

She broke off suddenly. "My lands," she said, "I haven't wasted so much time in five years."

She looked annoyed, and Jean turned to me anxiously. "I think you wanted to ask her for some specials for *Fashions of the Hour*, didn't you?" he asked.

There was an uncomfortable silence. "Quimper, was it?" he suggested finally. I clutched at it.

"That's right," I said eagerly. "I was so carried away by what you were telling me, I almost forgot."

Miss Lang sniffed. "Quimper's all right," she admitted grudgingly, "and we're doing very well with it. It's our own discovery, too. Still, I wouldn't want to see the China Section represented in *Fashions of the Hour* by earthenware."

"It's only for 'Little Things Noticed on a Walk through the Store,'" I assured her, hurriedly, and she was mollified.

"Well, in that case . . ." she said.

I asked her how Field's had discovered it. "I might be able to use it in a story," I added quickly, so that Miss Lang would feel justified in taking the time to tell me.

"Ethel Reeve," she said, "was in our Interior Decorating Department, and left to go to France with the Red Cross during the World War. She was down in a little seaside resort called Quimper and she found some national peasant red clay earthenware that had native pictures painted on it. She thought it was unusual and quaint. It was very crude. She had some shipped back to us, but when it came ninety per cent of it was broken. She was heartbroken; but she asked our Buyer to look for it the first trip he made after the war. He couldn't find a trace of it in Paris. He asked the Paris office to trace it and see if it was worth while to go to Quimper. They finally located it and he went down. He said he made the trip on the worst train in France, the 'Cootie Special,' he called it. But he found an old pottery where this earthenware was made. He placed an order that made the eyes of the natives down there bulge, I guess. He brought some of it back with him and showed it. Now you know what a rage it is."

Jean began suddenly to chuckle. "Remember our Rug Buyer," he asked Miss Lang, "who came back from the Far East with a tent and a sheik costume?"

Miss Lang nodded.

Jean turned to me. "He set up the tent in his department, and sat himself in front of it every afternoon, giving a lecture. The lectures only lasted three days; someone from the management happened to pass through the section and heard our Buyer expounding on the qualities of camel dung. While they lasted the talks were quite a rage. Drew a big crowd."

He caught Miss Lang's eye and suggested hurriedly he'd be glad to select with me the specific pieces to describe. Miss Lang gave her consent, adding she couldn't take more time away from customers anyway.

As we turned to go she called after us, warningly, "Now don't forget to pick what out-of-towners will like, cute, but not so extreme as Chicago taste."

While we were making our selections, I asked Jean about the importance of the out-of-town trade. He looked at me solemnly, setting down on the table a piece of Quimper he had been holding in his hand. "Don't you ever forget," he said, "how important the out-of-town trade is. It's what makes Marshall Field & Company the only store of its kind in the world, because Chicago is a crossroads. Everybody going east to west and west to east, comes through this city. Only they have a stopover, thank the Lord. There isn't a train that goes straight through Chicago. So where do these people go with a few hours over in Chicago? They go to the Art Institute and they come to Marshall Field & Company. They become our customers and they go on ordering from us when they go back home, no matter where they've come from.

"Why, take our Toy Department alone." He'd been very gay a minute before. Now he was fervent and solemn. "Take our Toy Department. It's the only one in the world that does a big year-round business. And I mean big. Do you know why?"

"The out-of-towners?" I suggested.

Jean nodded. "Taking presents home to the kids. And when you're writing *Fashions of the Hour* copy, keep those people in mind. First of all, figure it this way. We've got a lot of rich and stylish people here in Chicago, but they're not New Yorkers, and there's a difference. They're not quite so sophisticated—they don't want to be. But they're more sophisticated than the rich and stylish people from the smaller towns."

He picked up the piece of Quimper again. "Now this item . . ." he resumed, and I took it down in my notebook.

A few days later I had a request from Mr. Bunker, the head of the Linen Section, to come and see him when I had the time. Mr. Bunker was one of the most charming people in the store. I put on my hat and went down the moment I got his message.

He was, he said, in something of a spot about some merchandise. He wondered if up there on *Fashions of the Hour* we'd been cutting loose a little on some of his merchandise without telling him about it; we'd better get together on it. He was smiling as he said this, but I protested indignantly.

"We wouldn't dream of mentioning any kind of merchandise," I assured him vehemently, "without an OK from the head of that section."

He answered he'd been sure of that, but just the same he was puzzled. "Buffaloed," he said, by a sudden rush on silk sheets.

"On what?" I echoed. I'd never heard of them.

"I don't wonder you're surprised," he said, "but that's what they are, silk sheets."

I told him in the last few days I'd been hearing a lot about merchandising; sudden fads, and the difficulty of knowing when they began, and more important, when they were going to end. But I'd certainly never heard of silk sheets as a fad. "I've never even seen one."

"I'll show you one," he said, and brought out from some layers of tissue paper a pair of exquisite, hemstitched, crepe de Chine sheets in peach color. "I bought a couple of pairs," he explained, "the last time I was in Paris. I didn't expect to sell them. They run about five hundred dollars. But I thought they'd make a nice display item for our Spring Opening. All of a sudden in the last ten days, I've been swamped with orders for silk sheets. I don't know where they're coming from. I haven't even displayed these yet. I've been waiting for the opening."

"Who's ordering them?" I asked.

"That's another funny thing," was his answer, "not the real Carriage Trade. Names you wouldn't have heard of. Rich, but not real society. And the addresses are from all over Chicago. So it can't be one special group of people either."

I had no explanation for the mystery and went back up to the Bureau.

That day at lunch with some of the girls, I told them about Mr. Bunker's problem. Back in my office I telephoned him.

"I've got the answer," I said, "I learned it at lunch. Some of my friends from the Bureau stayed downtown for dinner the other night and went to the movies. I couldn't go. They saw the new Cecil B. DeMille picture with a closeup in it of the heroine in bed, and the bed's got silk sheets."

"That's it," Mr. Bunker broke in. "A Sears Roebuck man was telling me merchants ought to watch movies for merchandising trends."

"By the way," I added just as he was about to ring off, "how are you going to fill the orders?"

"I got the orders taken care of," he said, "before I even started tracking down the source. The Sisters at a convent here are doing the hemstitching and embroidering. They're pleased as Punch. The Mother Superior told me they've been praying for a way to get more money for their Day Nursery."

Achsah put off as long as she dared scheduling the photographs for the new *Fashions of the Hour*. But when Eva Le Gallienne came in a play to Chicago, and at another theater a well-known British comedienne opened in a comedy, Achsah said we must get them to pose for us. She sent me to negotiate because, she admitted candidly, she was shy about such interviews. So was I, but Achsah was my boss.

I found both Miss Le Gallienne and the other British actress charming, and agreeable to posing. An appointment in the store was made for each. Miss Le Gallienne's was the first.

When she arrived I took her immediately to a dressing room that had been made ready for her with clothes on display for her selection, all of them just arrived from Paris. As she examined them, Miss Le Gallienne grew more and more sad. The Buyer from each of the departments represented, with an assistant brought along to help put on the clothes, was on hand to assist

Miss Le Gallienne, each hoping hers would be the merchandise to be featured.

Miss Le Gallienne did not try on any of them. "I do not like fashionable clothes," she said wistfully. Since she was posing for a fashion magazine, Achsah and I, not to mention the Buyers, were somewhat taken aback. "Can you not let me pose just as myself?" she questioned.

Perhaps Achsah thought it would grate on Miss Le Gallienne's sensibilities to be told that a page in *Fashions of the Hour* represented a considerable amount of money and ought therefore to be devoted either to promoting Marshall Field & Company or the city of Chicago. The story accompanying the photograph would carry full publicity about the play in which Miss Le Gallienne was appearing and her own prestige as an actress, but the photograph itself should carry a little something of Marshall Field & Company, since Marshall Field could not supply Eva Le Gallienne to its customers.

Achsah, however, said none of this, but only suggested perhaps if we'd walk through the store, Miss Le Gallienne might find something to her liking in which she would consent to be photographed.

She agreed and we made an extended tour, while Mr. Hutchinson hopefully set up his camera and lights.

When we joined him, two hours later, Achsah was carrying over her arm an old mantilla from the Lace Department, and I, with the assistance of a porter from the Antique Section, was bearing a *prie-dieu*.

The photographing itself occupied three hours. It gave me time to think, while I waved lights and moved props under Mr. Hutchinson's direction, of the china on the shelves and the mah-jongg sets down in the Games Section. We didn't seem to be helping them to move but we were giving a big push to old mantillas and antique *prie-dieux*, of which the store had two in stock.

"I do not like fashionable clothes," she said wistfully.

"I do not like fashionable clothes," she said wistfully.

A few days later the British comedienne had her appointment. She loved all the clothes shown her, insisted she would like to be photographed in every outfit displayed to her. When she pulled off her dress to try on the first, the Buyer, her sales assistant and I were introduced to a display of the actress without any underwear whatsoever. Anything under a dress, she explained, made her feel uncomfortable. I asked, as I felt one of us should say something, if the texture of the wool dress she was wearing wasn't uncomfortable against her skin. It was not in the least, she assured us, and added, encouragingly, that if other people once tried wearing only a dress, they would never in the world go back to underclothing.

I thought of the anxiety in the Lingerie Section over an anticipated drop in the sale of Philippine underwear. I thought of the Corset Buyer's apprehension over a rumor of boneless girdles and the decline of stays. We would not, I decided as we covered up the charming British actress, precipitate in *Fashions of the Hour* an underwear and girdle decline into total oblivion.

# * 12 *

HELEN WELLS came to work for *Fashions of the Hour* on a morning when we were on our way to press. Achsah and I were just leaving her office, pressing each to her stomach a large bulk of OK'd copies in folders, drawings, cuts, page proofs, all the raw material of the coming issue.

The office boy came to Achsah's door. "Miss Wells to see you," he said.

Achsah gasped and dropped on her desk the entire load she had just assembled. "Merciful Heavens," she said, "I hired Helen Wells to work for us in the Art Department and I forgot all about her. Send her in." She began gathering again to her stomach the folders, muttering, "I can't stop for anybody."

We passed Helen Wells. She was coming in as we were going out. Achsah only paused. "Miss Wells," she said, "I'm delighted to have you with us, but we're on our way to press. When you've been here a little longer, you'll know what that means. I haven't time to explain anything to you. Just go into my office for the time being." She indicated it by a nod of her head. Her arms and hands were encircling the folders. "Answer the telephone and if anyone asks for us, say we're at the printer's. This is Emily Kimbrough."

Helen and I said "How do you do" to each other.

[ 176 ]

"Albert," she indicated the office boy, "will give you the tele-phone number of the printer's in case it's urgent. That's all. We may not see you for days. Good-by."

I turned back at the door. "Introduce yourself to the girls in the newspaper office," I called, "they'll take you to lunch."

Helen had not moved from the place in the office where we had met her, but she smiled dimly and nodded her head.

I hurried after Achsah.

In a taxi on the way to Donnelley's, Achsah reiterated her regret over the cursory welcome she had given Miss Wells. My own opinion was that, given a choice, I would have preferred a first day of sitting at the Editor's desk, my only responsibility saying into the telephone that the editor was away, to my own baptism of fire among the Buyers. But I kept my opinion to myself.

This printing session varied from the first only in detail and the absence of Mr. Donnelley and my father. Mr. Donnelley's absence was by choice, my father's had been maneuvered by Achsah's offer at my solicitation of a night's lodging with her at her family's apartment so that I would not have to go home alone.

We stopped work at three in the morning, went for a few hours' sleep to the Virginia Hotel where Achsah's mother and father had an apartment during the winter, and were back at Donnelley's at ten.

At breakfast in their sitting room Mrs. Gardner had told me how little she thought of Achsah's professional life, though she was thankful that at least it was at Marshall Field's. She had also delicately obtained from me the information that my parents were both living; having obtained it, she expressed with more vigor than delicacy a desire to know how they had come to allow a daughter to go to work in a store all day and go traipsing around printers until all hours of the night.

While we waited at Donnelley's for the first proofs to be pulled, I reminded Achsah of the conversation and added that for the sake of Mrs. Gardner's blood pressure, it would probably be wise if she and my mother did not meet. Achsah agreed, "But," she said, "I'd be willing to bet you right here and now, that in ten years' time, maybe even less, mother's point of view will be so a thing of the past that if what she said this morning were repeated, it wouldn't be believed."

I objected a little. "Your mother's point of view," I protested, "isn't unique. I hear it on all sides from the mothers of my friends. It's *my* mother's point of view that's different."

"It won't be," she answered. "Look at me. My father is not in business, so he and mother can go where they please. That's why we lived in Europe all the years I was growing up. Now they prefer to live in the old family house near St. Paul, where we came from originally. But they move down to a hotel here during the winter months just to make a home for me since I'm determined to have this crazy thing of a career. I go back with them to Hastings in the summer since we have no magazine coming out then. Mother represents an era in which women honestly believed that it was better for their daughters to be married to a drunkard or a scoundrel than be an old maid. Now, a great many girls who aren't married, and a lot of those choosing not to be married, are having lives of their own that are more exciting and stimulating than anything they dreamed could ever happen to them. That's very bewildering to parents, except to yours. The others don't know how to cope with their daughters who don't seem to need either pity or protection. So they grumble about it now but the grumbling is getting fainter. The protection is inconvenient to them and is making them look a little foolish, so that's going to stop. Parents who object to their daughters' working, and girls from our background who don't get jobs if they're not married, are all going out of fashion. I don't know anything that goes out faster than fashion."

A boy came to our table with the first pulled proofs, and we settled down to work. We divided the pages between us, Achsah checking with the Buyers' OK'd copy and rereading, for possible infringements of editorial and store policy, the articles from outside writers, and I filling in or taking out words to make a solid and even block of copy without a ragged runover, or "widow."

Suddenly Achsah interrupted me with an exclamation. "There's a discrepancy," she said, "in the Book column, in both title and price, between the original copy and the proof."

"Well," I said, "I'd go by the OK'd copy. If it's wrong it's the section's responsibility. We haven't got time to take this proof over to them."

"We haven't got an OK'd copy." Achsah's voice had a hollow sound.

Mine was a more hollow echo. "We haven't?"

Achsah shook her head. "They send up their own material. We don't go to Mrs. Hahner. She sends to us what she wants and when she wants it. But when we were getting our first proofs back in the store I should have sent one down for checking and her official OK." She groaned and put her head between her hands. "Why couldn't this have happened with an easy Buyer? Why Mrs. Hahner?" She raised her head. "Well," she said briskly and resignedly, "there's nothing for it. You or I will just have to go, and it's going to hold up all these pages and the presses for hours."

I had a sudden recollection of a girl with red hair. "Who's that girl you left at your telephone yesterday?" I asked. "She's probably still there."

"My Lord," Achsah answered, "Helen Wells. Of course. Poor child, this is a rough assignment for her, but it's a life-saver for us."

My feeling was that Helen's introduction was now approaching the level mine had established. Achsah was on the telephone. From where I sat I could hear it answered.

"*Fashions of the Hour,*" the voice said, "Miss Wells speaking," and when Achsah had identified herself, a long sigh and the receiver fairly cracked with the pleasure in the voice that came over it. "Oh, Miss Gardner," it said, "I'm *so* glad to hear you."

Achsah hoped, she said glumly, Miss Well's pleasure would continue, but doubted it, and then gave instructions for her to take a taxi immediately to Donnelley's, pick up pages we were holding and take them back. Achsah drew a deep breath and cleared her throat. "Take them," she said, "to Mrs. Hahner, who is the head of the Book Department. Tell her there has been an oversight in getting her OK on copies she sent up to *Fashions of the Hour*. Tell her I am personally responsible for this. Make it clear to her you have had nothing to do with it. This is very important, Miss Wells, for your sake. But also insist she take the time to go over the copy immediately and give you a corrected sheet or an OK. Explain we are at the printer's and every minute is precious. Is that clear?"

Achsah hung up and turned to me. "You have no idea," she said somberly, "what I have asked that girl to do. You've never met Mrs. Hahner."

She put the copy from the Book Section in an envelope, wrote Miss Helen Wells across the face of it and gave it to a boy to take down to the door, with instructions that it be handed to Miss Wells on her arrival so that she wouldn't even take time to leave the taxi.

Some time during the afternoon the telephone on our table rang. Achsah answered it but I could hear the voice coming through. It belonged to Miss Wells but it had lost its earlier lilt. I couldn't make out the words. Achsah listened and I saw her lips tighten. Finally she said, "I'm just as sorry as I can be, my dear. I didn't know it would be quite that bad, but there was nothing else to do. Stay there, and I'll call you back." She hung up and immediately took off the receiver again and asked for State 1000, the Field number.

While she waited for the connection she muttered to me, "I

[ 180 ]

don't like battling with Marcella Hahner, but this time she's not going to get away with it."

A minute or two later she was talking to her. "Marcella," she said, "this is Achsah Gardner. I sent a new member of the *Fashions of the Hour* staff to you a little while ago with a page to be OK'd. You seem to have wiped up the floor with her and reduced her to tears. I hope you're satisfied. As far as we're concerned, it doesn't make the slightest difference to us whether your column on Books is run or not. We have plenty of material to fill up the space. If you want Books represented, get that copy checked and OK'd and over to me at R. H. Donnelley's inside of an hour. If I don't have it by then, we'll go on without it. I hope you'll take this up with the management. And just one more thing—the next time you want to fight, why don't you pick on someone your own size?"

She hung up and turned to me, her eyes round with astonishment. "Mercy," she said, "I've never done such a thing as that in my life. I feel wonderful."

She picked up the telephone again, called her office, got Helen Wells and said, "Miss Wells, will you telephone Mrs. Hahner's secretary? Tell her to let you know if an OK'd proof is coming for *Fashions of the Hour.* If you get a message within an hour that it is, go down to the Book Section again, pick it up, bring it to me here. I'm terribly sorry you had such a bad time, but I want to tell you one thing more and you think it over. If you can't face going down to the Book Section again to pick up that proof, then, my dear, working in the Advertising Department of a department store is not for you."

In a little less than an hour the OK'd Book column was in front of Achsah, brought by Helen Wells. And a few minutes after that, the new member of the *Fashions of the Hour* staff was sitting at the table with us, reading proof and checking copy.

The three of us went to dinner at a near-by restaurant, and at two in the morning Helen and I shared a taxi to the South Side, discovering we were neighbors. We had already become friends.

The magazine was on the press. We were well into the makeup of the next issue, the Summer Number, when Achsah received via house mail one morning an application from the Book Section for a page on suggested vacation reading. Achsah showed me the paper and pointed to the note written at the bottom. I read, "Dear Achsah, I'd like to talk this page over with you at your convenience. Always affectionately, Marcella."

"Those are peace terms," was Achsah's comment, "and I'm certainly going to accept them fast."

But that night Achsah was unexpectedly called away to St. Paul. She telephoned me that evening her instructions to take over the magazine until she got back and the reminder of Mrs. Hahner's request. "Maybe you think I'm leaving town on purpose, because of that," she ended. "It's a low, demeaning thought, and you ought to be ashamed of yourself. But good luck to you," and she hung up.

I had been entertaining a young man when she called, but after I returned to him from the telephone, my entertainment value dropped so low as not to register at all, and my caller left shortly after. I was barely aware of his departure. I was preoccupied with the anticipation of Mrs. Hahner.

The next morning as soon as I reached the office, while my courage was as near the sticking point as I could bring it, I telephoned the Book Section for an appointment. Word came back I would be received at eleven-thirty. At eleven-twenty-five on my way out of the Bureau, I paused for an affectionate and melancholy farewell with each of my friends there.

My gloomiest expectations of the interview were filled to the brim. Mrs. Hahner was at the Fiction Counter talking to my friend, Harriet Smith, when I came into the section. I did not know that the five-foot-tall, rather plump, extremely pretty, little woman talking to Harriet was the head of Marshall Field's

Book Section. But Harriet was a friend of mine and I intended to ask her the whereabouts of Mrs. Hahner's office. I stood near by waiting for the conversation to end and noticed how startlingly white the little woman's hair was in contrast to her pink cheeks and smooth young skin.

Harriet suddenly caught sight of me and said, "Hello there. Mrs. Hahner, this is Emily Kimbrough. She's Miss Gardner's assistant on *Fashions of the Hour*."

The little woman whirled around and looked me up and down. Her eyes were blue and sharp.

"How do you do, Mrs. Hahner," I said quaveringly. "I have an appointment with you. I was just going to ask Harriet the way to your office."

"I'll show you the way to my office," Mrs. Hahner answered, and her voice was as cold as the lip of scorn. "I've got a few things to say to you there." She turned on her heel—they were very high heels—and moved toward the far end of the section in short steps, so fast it was almost a run.

Harriet and I exchanged a look of understanding sympathy before I followed.

I did not catch up with Mrs. Hahner because I preferred not to. I stayed at her heels, but all the length of the section I could hear her, and so could the customers and clerks near by.

"I won't have it," was one of the sentiments she threw out, "sending down any new girl they've got up there. They're all ignorant and they're all fresh," she told a startled customer. "They take up my time and then they try to tell me—*me*—how to advertise." She pointed to herself dramatically, pausing in front of a young man who up to that moment had been browsing among the fine bindings counters. The young man dropped the book he had been leafing and took on the nervous stance of a basketball player endeavoring to dodge a guard and make for a distant goal.

Mrs. Hahner thwarted him. Matching her footwork to his, she

remained directly in front of him and said in a soft, wooing voice, "I don't believe anyone's taken care of you. May I?"

It was so far as to be unrecognizable from the tone that had proclaimed my shortcomings less than a minute before. I slipped from behind her to the shelter of a pile of books on a near-by display table. I wanted to effect for myself the exit the young man had been trying for. But of two dismal prospects, I preferred taking up where Mrs. Hahner had left off to beginning again. Therefore, I waited.

The young man gave up his plan and waited too. Mrs. Hahner eased him back to the table he had quitted and picked up the book he'd dropped. She put it under her arm, placed both hands on the table behind her, gave a quick jump and landed on its surface. She crossed her ankles and swung her feet, and I saw then how tiny her feet were and how delicate her ankles. I saw the young man notice this too. She withdrew the book from under her arm, rubbed a hand over its leather binding, patted the volume affectionately and looked up at the young man with a tender smile.

"You've been looking at one of my favorite books," she told him. "I bought that in London and had it specially bound. Just for myself, really. I remember thinking to myself at the time, 'Now, Marcella, this is just another of your foolish whims. You ought to buy things because they'll sell, not because *you* love them.' I gave myself really a very bad scolding and it didn't do a bit of good. And now here you are going over that very particular volume. Do tell me honestly, do you like it a little, or was I as foolish as my conscience told me I was?"

The young man mumbled happily something about it's not seeming foolish to him at all. That, on the contrary, he thought it was wonderful there was a place in America where you could find unusual books.

Mrs. Hahner assured him to hear that made her happier than anything anyone had told her in a long time. In fact the only

"I don't believe anyone's taken care of you. May I?"

other person who had said that to her had been her dear, dear friend in England, Willie.

The young man smirked happily but appeared to expect something more in the way of explanation, and Mrs. Hahner gave it bountifully. Willie Maugham," she explained gently. "My dear, dear friend, Willie Maugham. Do you by any chance know him? Isn't he a darling?"

The young man's eyes widened. "Is that W. Somerset Maugham?" he asked hesitantly.

"But of course, my dear," she answered quickly. "Who else? You don't know him then?"

The young man shook his head.

Mrs. Hahner leaned forward so that she could put her tiny hand on his coat sleeve and her face close to his. "Oh, but you must. You and he would get on beautifully together, each of you loving my little volume. When he comes over next time, I shall have a party for him. He always comes straight to me, you know, as soon as he can get out of New York, and I always have a party for him, but very small, you understand, and only very special people, because I know Willie so well, and just the sort of people he expects me to have for him."

Using the young man's arm as a lever, she lowered herself gracefully and nimbly to the ground, slipped her arm through his and turned him toward the back of the room. "Now," she instructed, "if you will come with me, I'm going to write down your name and address so I can invite you to Willie's party, and shan't we take along your and my special volume?"

The young man spluttered his acquiescence like bursts from a Roman candle. "Oh, yes—my, yes—surely—thank you."

"And while we're back there," she continued over his candle bursts, "I'm going to show you one or two other very special little books I don't believe I've ever shown to anyone before, because, to tell you the truth, I've been afraid I might have to let them go. And they're so much a part of me. But when someone comes along who seems to have that kind of secret, special communication, then I can't hold my own secrets any longer."

They disappeared from my sight and hearing, Mrs. Hahner with her arm still slipped through the young man's. I stayed where I was because of an intuitive sense Mrs. Hahner would prefer it that way.

In about twenty minutes they were back. The young man carried a package that must have contained at least six volumes, all of them, I felt sure, very special. He moved like a smiling sleepwalker. Mrs. Hahner's arm was through his. As they came abreast of where I stood behind the display table, she patted his hand two or three times, turned him in the direction of the elevators and withdrew her arm. "Good-by," she said. "You'll come again, won't you? And we'll have that party for Willie."

Hearing only the sound of her voice without the words, I could have believed it was Jane Cowl on Juliet's balcony.

"I don't know how to thank you," the young man told her fervently. "I'm certainly coming back. It's been wonderful."

He started off; his feet interfered a little at first, but he untangled them after a lurch or two and was presently caught up in the crowd surging toward an open elevator.

Mrs. Hahner wheeled around to me. I had thought she didn't know I was there. She resumed instantly the tone of the conversation and the tone of voice she had dropped at sight of the young man. She resumed also her former line of march and I fell in behind her. "And when I say I want to talk to someone on *Fashions of the Hour*," she began, "I mean Achsah, and not some young whippersnapper coming down here to cut her teeth."

Her office was at the far end of the Book Department tucked away behind the rare books and fine bindings room. She went immediately to her desk and sat down behind it. The desk was large and piled with books, but somehow Mrs. Hahner was not dwarfed. Perhaps her anger blew her into larger-than-life stature, because she seemed to me, standing in front of her, to enlarge rather than dwindle. I would not have said I had let myself be distracted from her for one instant, yet somehow I encompassed a sufficient view of the walls of the room to see they were lined with signed photographs. I dared not let my eye rest on any one of them long enough to identify the subjects, but I would have laid a confident wager they were all famous authors.

Mrs. Hahner had been silent as she went to the desk and for a second or two after seating herself there. It proved to be only for the purpose of gathering breath and further ammunition for attack. When the attack was launched, it was a dressing-down such as I had never in my life experienced. I was the object of scorn and derision and fury. I epitomized the Advertising Bureau and that in turn was the crystallization of all that in her business life she hated most. We were all inefficient, arrogant, we lied, we cheated, we were jealous of her, we would resort to any measures to discredit her, even to running her out of the store in order to take over her department. And she dared us to. We were as good as trying to teach her her business. Why didn't we come out frankly and say we'd like to get rid of her? And one of us young college jackasses take over and show Marshall Field & Company how much smarter any one of us was than Marcella Hahner who had built up the biggest retail book business in the world?

Suddenly I was angry. I was fighting, furiously mad. I had been dreading an interview and meeting with Mrs. Hahner. I had been genuinely frightened at the very prospect of it. I had been close to panic at the moment of actually meeting her, by reason of its unexpectedness at Harriet Smith's Fiction Counter. But standing in front of the desk and facing Mrs. Hahner, blasted by this tirade, I was, to my own astonishment, "boiled."

That is what on a summer holiday at the seashore we call it, when a wave catches you unexpectedly, rolls over you, knocks you down and spins you into shore, gasping for breath and not knowing where you are. It was exactly like that for me. I was boiled by the rage that came over me.

Shaken, and scarcely knowing where I was, I turned and stumbled toward the door. Mrs. Hahner called after me. "Where do you think you're going?"

I knew then exactly where I was and turned back to her. "I'm going up to my office," I said. "I don't intend to be talked to like this by anyone. Not ever. I work for Field's, and Field's can *fire* me, but nobody can do *this*."

I started for the door again and had reached it, when a quiet, serene voice behind me queried, "How about going to lunch with me?"

I looked around. Her face had broken up into wrinkles at the corners of her eyes and mouth, making parentheses around a broad, generous, humorous grin. "I've got an Irish temper," she said, "because I'm Irish."

I had not, I am sure, hit anyone since I had passed the age of ten, but I very nearly had cause to report to my parents that evening that I had clouted a woman twice my age. I did not, however, have to make that humiliating announcement. I went instead to lunch with Mrs. Hahner.

On my way up to my office for my bag, gloves and coat, I passed Harriet Smith at the Fiction Counter. She called after me and I went over. "The boss wipe up the floor with you?" she asked.

I nodded my head but neither paused nor looked in her direction. I was almost out of the section and out of hearing when her voice reached me again faintly, with the question, "Where's she taking you to lunch?"

# * 13 *

MARCELLA HAHNER taught me more than anyone at Field's except my boss, Achsah Gardner, and became a dear and fiercely loyal friend. At lunch with her on the day we met she told me she had come to the store in 1915 when the Book Section had only recently emerged from a few counters in the Toys division to a full-fledged department. The Wanamaker Stores had been pioneers in giving books this importance, and Wanamaker's was the only rival organization on which Field's kept a watchful and respectful eye.

When I met Marcella only a little over ten years after the establishment of the department she had built it into the biggest retail book business in the world, and herself into the Czarina of Marshall Field & Company, all book publishers and all authors. To book salesmen, the representatives of publishing houses, she was a combination of Simon Legree and Mary Pickford. The people in her own section adored her, respected her, and were scared to a pulp of her. She had established and she maintained her absolute sovereignty over publishers by the artful device of selling more of their books than any other retailer even approached. Every other bookseller the country over based his order on the number of volumes Mrs. Hahner had requested.

Book salesmen became her humble subjects for this persuasive reason.

If Mrs. Hahner liked a book she made it a best seller. If she liked an author she made anything that author wrote a best seller. Carl Sandburg's *The Prairie Years* was published in 1926. It was a beautiful book, but it cost $10, and its author had not then a following comparable to Zane Grey's. Mrs. Hahner read an advance copy of *The Prairie Years*, clasped it passionately to her bosom, and placed an initial order for one thousand copies, to the hysterical astonishment of the publishers. Other booksellers had marked it as a volume of prestige but no selling value, and therefore warranting only a very small order.

When the news of Marcella's plunge was relayed to them, as quickly as the publishers had recovered their powers of articulation, the little orders were instantly stepped up proportionately to Marshall Field's, and Mr. Sandburg soared to the financial stratum sparsely populated by Zane Grey and a few other writing inhabitants.

Clara Laughlin, a Chicago woman, was a friend of Marcella Hahner's, and complained one day that she was unable to find the kind of guidebook to Europe she wanted for a young relative about to make a first trip abroad.

"Well, why don't you write the kind of book you want, Clara?" was Marcella's crisp answer, "and I'll sell it."

She sold *So You're Going to Paris* by Clara Laughlin and the subsequent *So You're Going to*—— series in a quantity standard travel books had required years to achieve, and put the Laughlin guides on a par with fiction best sellers all over the country.

She was the first bookseller to personalize an author to his public. Before the Marshall Field & Company Book Fair in 1919 an author, had his readers thought of him at all, had been a blurred figure without personality, but Mrs. Hahner in the winter of 1918 went to the Coliseum in Chicago to see the Automobile Show, not because she was interested in automobiles but because

She was the first bookseller to personalize an author to his public.

a friend had taken her. Sitting pensively on the running board of a car on display and bored by her surroundings, she began to ruminate on what brought people by the thousands to see the show and did not bore them. She came to the conclusion rapidly, because she was Irish, that the reason for the public's interest was that automobiles were being personalized by their manufacturers. She leaped from that conclusion to a comparable possibility in the book business. Automobile designers corresponded to authors, manufacturers were the publishers, dealers, Marshall Field & Company, and the public always the same.

Twenty-four hours later she had from Marshall Field & Company executives full endorsement of a Book Fair and had further anesthetized them into giving her a very comfortable appropriation for it. The following day she was in New York badgering, cajoling and commanding publishers to be like automobile manufacturers and come to her show.

When the Fair opened, fifty-six publishers were represented with booths, and in these, exhibits ranging from a cut of the original clay prism of the Royal Annals of Sennacherib, 689 B.C., to modern manuscripts and live authors. The authors spoke and autographed their books for thousands of people, most of whom until Marcella brought their attention to the matter had never owned nor particularly wanted to own an autographed copy of anything. And ever since that Marshall Field & Company carnival an author, on the day his book is published, has left the seclusion that his typewriter grants and gone to sit in other carnival tents wherever his publisher sends him to cry his wares and endorse his product.

No wonder publishers and authors had dreams that Marcella was summoning them and sprang trembling from their beds. And yet, they liked her. Many of them treasured a deep and genuine affection for her. All of them respected her and most of them owed something of their success to her.

Many Chicagoans must have seen her one day in a taxi driving up Michigan Avenue or around Lincoln Park with a gaunt scare-crow of a man. Several times, Marcella said, telling me the story and hugging herself, a particular gesture of hers when she was delighted, a policeman had stopped the taxi alerted by reports to him of a couple seen battling, shouting at the top of their lungs, waving their arms at each other. Each time they were stopped she was recognized, and the taxi was permitted to drive on. The other occupant was Sinclair Lewis, and they were not fighting, they were dear friends, speaking aloud simultaneously their ideas on writing.

Harriet Smith, John Sheeley, Loretta, Marcella's secretary whose last name I never heard, and Rose Oller, assistant head of the department, were the people working for Marcella that I knew best. They could break her down, because they knew her so well, into all her separate unrelated parts, the way a painter breaks down with his eye a subject he is going to translate to canvas, and reassemble her each time with astonishment into a capricious, wise, warm, generous, ruthless, shrewd, impulsive, calculating woman, five feet one inch tall.

Harriet could have told me the day I met Marcella that I would be scored like an ear of corn by Marcella's tongue and then asked to lunch, and that the chances were ninety-nine to one, no one in the section even willing to lay a bet on it, I would go to lunch and on my return hope I'd be asked again. That was the boss's technique, she explained to me: blow her lungs out at you, be sorry and take you to lunch. Harriet's own experience had been something like mine, though she had counted it advisable not to tell me of it until I should have had my own. Hers had occurred shortly after she'd gone to Field's to work.

One day a customer had complained about Harriet's service to Mrs. Hahner, who had happened to come along as the sale was being made. Mrs. Hahner had promptly defended Harriet vehe-mently and sent the customer scuttling apologetically out of the section. Immediately the customer was out of earshot Mrs.

Hahner had turned on Harriet and, in Harriet's words, torn her apart. When she felt the disintegration complete, Mrs. Hahner had said briskly, "Now go to the washroom and pull yourself together, and I'll take you to lunch." That, Harriet had learned, was the established pattern.

Another fixed custom of Marcella's I learned from Harriet and from Ollie. The little boss, they said, could spot instantly when someone in the section was having trouble of any sort. She would call that member of her department into her office, hand across the desk a sum of money, always in cash, and say, "I know you're in some kind of trouble. This will help *any* kind. If you want to tell me, go ahead, maybe I can advise you or help in other ways. But you don't have to tell me."

Loretta's desk was just outside Mrs. Hahner's office, with a partition between that did not go all the way up to the ceiling. Loretta told me she's heard Mrs. Hahner say this to so many people, she'd lost track long ago of the number of times it had happened, but even the words were just about the same always.

She'd heard McSweeney, an accountant in the section, remonstrate with Mrs. Hahner about handing out money. That had happened almost as regularly as payday coming round, and every time Mrs. Hahner had answered, "Don't bother me with that nonsense. Anybody can say he's sorry you're in trouble. It may help, but money *proves* you're sorry, and money *always* helps."

This was only one of the reasons the people who worked for her, though scared of her, couldn't have been bribed by an offer of twice the pay they might get at Field's to work for anyone else.

"Except when she's bawling you out," Harriet explained when I stopped in one day for a chat, "she makes you feel you're important. She wants to learn what anybody in the section can tell her. She's like a child that way, not a stuck-up head of a section."

I asked Harriet if she herself had friends in other sections. "A few," she said, "but not many." She grinned a little self-consciously. "I guess the truth of it is we feel superior to the

[ 197 ]

other people in the store. That's the boss's fault too. She tells us we are. This department is like an island. We're independent, nobody interferes with us. The boss does her own hiring and firing. The Personnel man doesn't send anybody down to be placed here. He wouldn't dare."

I asked Harriet if the boss did much actual selling.

Harriet grinned. "Not unless the customer is a good-looking man," she answered, "but she's certainly got a kind of sixth sense about that. Let a handsome male step into this department and she's out of her office and on the floor before he can so much as read the title on a paper jacket of a book. And if anyone of us has stepped up to him, she gives a nod that means 'Beat it,' and we do."

Another day, down for a little gossip in the section, I asked Ollie about the setup of the department. "Well," she said, "I'm the assistant to the boss. You know that. But this is a department where there's no question about just who is the boss, and there's a big gap between the boss and assistant, though she's fought for me in the front office every step of the way to where I am. More salary from them, more authority for me," Ollie smiled. "But there's only one real authority and everybody knows it.

"Now," she went on, "let's see about the rest of the setup. We have a sponsor like other sections. That's a kind of liaison person between the department and Personnel Office. The sponsor sees that the girls are dressed properly, the merchandise is well taken care of; but that job doesn't amount to much here because the boss knows more about her people than any sponsor, and is a lot fussier about taking care of merchandise. At the same time, she drives the management crazy in the matter of taking care of merchandise, because it's always being reported to them that our people are going home at night, loaded up with books. That's when the boss really starts hitting on all fours. If her people don't take merchandise out at night, she tells the management in no uncertain terms, she'll fire them. Her merchandise happens to be books. And she expects her salespeople to know what's inside of them, and how are they going to know if they don't read them? And if they spend their daytime reading, how are they going to sell? She pushes her sales records under their noses and the management shuts up pretty quick until the next time."

"I suppose you know," Ollie added, "we have the best 'plus sale' record in the store."

This was a new phrase to me, not as yet entered in my little notebook of store vocabulary, and I asked what it meant.

She was a little taken aback by my ignorance. "Why," she said, "I'm surprised you don't know that. In the first place it means having right at hand the merchandise requested. In our case with books, you can imagine that means keeping up your stock pretty well, to be able to lay your hand on a volume requested. Right away the customer is pleased. And this is what the boss drills into everybody. You move in immediately with some comment on the book and use that as a pretext to discuss other books, and put your hand on those as fast as you can, so in the end you've made a plus sale; the book requested *and* additional ones."

I realized then, I admitted to Ollie, I had never asked Harriet Smith for a specific book that I hadn't gone out of the section with two or three additional ones.

Ollie was not impressed. "That's nothing," she said. "You ought to see Harriet on a rainy day, when she really piles up her business. Lots of sections use a rainy day for calling the salespeople together in conferences on selling and merchandising. Buyers get their opinions on what items have gone well, what they'd like the Buyer to go out for in the New York market on the next trip—that kind of business. They just accept a sales loss on a rainy day. But you don't get Harriet into any conference. She's at the telephone with a list of her own customers beside her. And that list is almost as big as the telephone directory of a small town. She goes right through it, calling these people up, suggesting that since the weather is bad they're probably shut in at home and wouldn't they like a good book to read? Some new ones have come in recently she could particularly recommend to that customer. By the time she's got to the end of her list, we've got special messengers on the run, deliveries going out in all directions. At the end of the day she hands in a sales total that would make a store executive think we were running a basement bargain sale, if he didn't know we don't do that sort of thing.

"The boss doesn't hold with cut prices and bargain sales. She's hell on getting good discounts and that's a Marshall Field policy. And she'll wear a publisher down until she gets it. But at the same time she places a bigger initial order than any retailer in the country. She'll put in an order as big as a jobber's, but she'll have nothing to do with bargain sales."

Marcella was the only Buyer who ever asked me to lunch. Ollie never did, though we were good friends. Ollie was sometimes brusque when the boss had been riding her, but never volatile like Marcella; she was steady, kind, thoughtful, with quick perceptiveness, and kindly humor. She was loved by every book salesman who came into the section, a tribute that was not paid Mrs. Hahner. Ollie was pretty, too, though not so striking-looking as Marcella. But she was of much the same build, short and a little plump. Instead of white hair that was Marcella's dramatic feature, Ollie's was dark, soft and curly. Ollie's eyes were brown and warm. Marcella's were blue and not warm. Ollie had sound, steady judgment, Marcella had flair.

Marcella and I got into a habit of lunching together, at least once a week. And if she had a visiting author, she would summon me for lunch or tea or perhaps just down to her office for talk.

I always accepted these invitations because they were royal commands, and because her voice on the telephone saying, "Come down, Emily, I've got an author," was saying for me "Open sesame" and opening a door on a treasure as rich as Ali Baba ever blinked at. People I never dreamed I might meet, stimulating, exciting talk, hilarious fun. And education in the craft of writing more valuable than any course I had ever taken at college given by these writing men, generously, passionately, and unconsciously because they were only talking delightedly to Marcella.

I met Somerset Maugham and Hugh Walpole, Mr. Galsworthy, John Drinkwater. There were so many of them who visited Marcella, and she was kindness itself to me, making it possible for me to meet and listen to these giants.

James Stephens came to my office with me one day after he and I had lunched with Marcella. He wanted to see, he said, where I worked. A few days later he sent me a bag of bright pebbles, "because," he wrote, "you are surely not safe from getting lost in that wonderful store, without something to guide you. Drop these along the way between you and Marcella, so you'll be able to reach an author." And in my office that day he'd said wistfully, "I see you have books here. I have books at home too, but not so many as I once had. And that's because people used to borrow my books and not return them. So I said to myself, 'I will write my name in my books and then my friends will bring them back where they belong.' But just after I had done that I had a little success, and my name became a little known. And so the people who had my books with my name in them kept them, and now I've scarcely a book *to* my name."

Tea in Marcella's office, after the store closed, was an indication of her special honor to a visitor. The tearoom would send down, before closing time, sandwiches and little cakes. The tea itself would be brewed in Marcella's office. I delighted in Marcella's office parties; and the relaxed way in which the guest of honor invariably settled back in a comfortable leather armchair was a rewarding endorsement of Marcella's pattern of entertaining.

I would come down to one of these parties, after work. The store would be emptied of customers, the lighting dimmed, the Book Section empty of people save a few cleaning women. Blue and white dust sheets spread over the display tables, made strange shapes of the piles of books underneath and the stiff cardboard posters that advertised them. It was a little like walking among the queer formations in the Garden of the Gods I had visited once in Colorado.

Crossing the threshold into Marcella's office at the end of that passage nearly always made me remember sharply how it had been at college to come into my room at the end of a hard working day, walking from the library or the science building at dusk across the dim deserted campus to reach my dormitory. In Marcella's office the lamps were lighted on her desk and on the small tables beside each of the four or five comfortable armchairs there. The smell of steam was in the air, the teakettle bubbling over an electric plate. Sandwiches and little cakes, cups and saucers, sugar and cream were on a table covered with an exquisite teacloth in the center of the room. Marcella cared about her accessories, and also had an eye to standing in well with Charley Bunker, head of the Linen Department, by displaying his merchandise. Charley was on solid terms with the executives on the ninth floor.

When the party was complete, there were never more than half a dozen people, Marcella, the guest of honor, his wife, when Marcella found that inclusion unavoidable. If one of these parties was given for a lady author, I never heard of it. Ollie was always there, and generally a literary critic or two from the newspapers, sometimes a special crony of Marcella's from outside the store. Marcella had no store cronies. I always telephoned mother when I was going to one of these teas, because I knew the party would not be over until seven o'clock at the earliest. Sometimes, when the talk was particularly good, Ollie, at a signal from Marcella, would slip out of the office and telephone for sandwiches and coffee to be sent in from a near-by restaurant, and then we might go on until late at night.

I would store away the talk, packing it down in my memory for the moment when I reached home; and mother, helping me off with my hat and coat in her impatience, waiting eagerly to hear, would say, "Well, what is he like as a person? Was there good conversation? Tell me about it."

That would be like slipping the catch on a toy I once had, a long, coiled-up snake in a tiny box, that slithered out the minute the catch was released and kept on coming from the tiny receptacle.

Sometimes I was turned away at the last minute from these parties, but when that happened it was for the particular reason that Marcella had become displeased with the guest of honor.

One afternoon, when I had been looking forward particularly to meeting after work at tea a distinguished author, from his photograph a benign, saintly old gentleman, and from his writings a gentle, lovable soul, Marcella telephoned me a little before five. "Don't come down to tea today," she ordered tersely, ". . . the old goat," and hung up.

I learned later that Ollie had gone to his hotel room with books for him to autograph, and to bring him to the store for the party, getting him past the watchman at the door.

"Within five minutes after I got there," Ollie said (I'd gone down to the section the next day to find out what had happened and heard the story direct), "*less* than five minutes after I got there," Ollie repeated, "and I'd just put down the books on the desk for him to autograph and was bending over, opening them up to the fly leaf to make it handy for him, that saintly old man jumped to his feet. The next thing I knew, he was chasing me around the room. He's certainly agile for his age. I got out of there in the nick of time."

Another tea party from which I was turned away was for an author who, early in the day, had been confronted in his hotel suite by an inexorable Marcella, leading a corps of Marshall Field delivery men. In a series of trips to and from a Field delivery van they stacked around the author eight thousand volumes to be autographed. The author's hysterical rage at the prospect of the task before him, and Marcella's determination that it should be done, created an impasse; but Marcella dissolved it by sending out for whisky. This was the era of Prohibition, a matter of small moment to Marcella when she was embarked on a purpose.

The whisky arrived in short order and was administered to the author at intervals during the day. By late afternoon he had signed the eight-thousandth volume, but was neither in the mood for, nor able physically to be conveyed by any method to, a tea party.

The reason I did not go to the party for Mr. G. K. Chesterton was that Mr. Chesterton annoyed Marcella, and Marcella sent word up to me at half-past five there would be no party.

I had been looking forward to meeting Mr. Chesterton. Marcella, I knew, had been in a pleasant flurry of anticipation too, because she had told me at least three times how surprised Mr. Chesterton was going to be to find one place in America where his tea was going to be as he would have had it in England—hot, strong and with very thin bread-and-butter sandwiches. There had, however, seemed more the atmosphere of a drizzle than a flurry around her voice when she had called me the day of the party to say she had just learned that Mrs. Chesterton was accompanying the great man. I doubted, however, that her presence was what had caused Marcella to cancel the whole party. It would have been far more likely to have caused an enlargement, if anything, in order to provide enveloping entertainment for Mrs. Chesterton while Marcella took over the guest of honor.

Ollie came up to my office the next day to tell me why the party had been nipped in the bud. She'd come up to me, Ollie explained, because she didn't want me to find out about it down in the section for fear we'd be seen, and that wouldn't be good for either of us. Mr. and Mrs. Chesterton had come, Ollie explained, Mr. Chesterton looking exactly like his photograph and Mrs. Chesterton like Queen Mary, only smaller, simpler and rounder. Mr. Chesterton had settled back in the best armchair and begun to talk. While he was talking he had pulled out his glasses that were hung on a wide black ribbon and had been tucked into his waist coat pocket. He had polished them a long time, a minute or two, Ollie computed; probably, she said, because he was talking so hard he wasn't noticing what he was doing. Then he'd adjusted them across the bridge of his nose and looked around. Almost immediately after that he'd become preoccupied, though the boss, Ollie asserted, had never been in better form.

"Telling about her Irish Uncle in Monroe, Michigan?" I interpolated, to get the picture clear.

Ollie nodded. "Of course. But Mr. Chesterton didn't seem to be particularly taken by the tale. He just sat staring out through the door, seemed to be kind of ruminating. Finally, Marcella got up from behind her desk and strolled around the room still talking, until she got behind his chair, so she was in focus with him for whatever he was looking at." Ollie paused. "Do you know what it was? The legs of that new little secretary Marcella just hired to help Loretta. She was at a desk just outside the boss's office, sitting with her legs crossed, swinging one on top of the other, waiting for the bell to ring so she could go home. The boss gave me every detail."

"I should have thought," I said in a little bewilderment, "Marcella would have been amused by that."

"Amused?" Ollie echoed. "With the pride the boss takes in her own legs? Like fun she was amused. She gave them each one cup of tea and while Mrs. Chesterton was saying it was by far the best tea she'd had in America, the boss was hustling her and her husband out of that office and on their way to the elevator."

Marcella telephoned me about a week after the Chesterton visit. She seemed her gay self again and wanted me to go to lunch. But *Fashions of the Hour* was coming to a boil again. We were getting ready to go to press, and I was not taking out time enough for lunch.

Three weeks later the magazine had been put to press, and in the lull that followed, before we began gathering up material for the next number, I went down one morning to the Book Section to see Marcella and learn what had been going on. Whenever any of us in the Advertising Bureau had been too tied up to get down through the store, we were always in a fever, as soon as the tension relaxed, to find out what had been going on and what tidbits we had missed.

Harriet Smith signaled to me as I came into the section. She was busy with a customer and I waited at her counter until she had finished. "Well," she said as soon as the customer had gone, "where've you been?"

"Having another issue," I told her, "but it's put to bed now. What's going on?"

"Plenty," she answered, nodding her head several times. "They decided about two weeks ago to set up the Victrola Section right next door to us. They put it in over last week end, and the boss has been wild ever since. She's really on a tear."

I asked why, and Harriet admitted she didn't exactly know. "I think it's pleasant. Hearing that music in the distance is kind of soothing. But the boss says it's a hell of a racket and disturbing to customers who want to browse. Personally, I think she's just mad because she wasn't consulted first. They've put something over on her in the store and she doesn't take that. I understand from Ollie she went straight up to the ninth floor and told the executives she wouldn't have it. And they told her it was none of her business."

Harriet nodded her head again several times. "And they think they can get away with that."

I asked what Harriet thought Marcella was going to do. "You've come just at the right minute," was her answer, "you couldn't have timed it better."

Ollie and John Sheeley came along the aisle and joined us. "Who let you in on this?" was Ollie's greeting to me.

I told her I hadn't the slightest idea what I was in on, but I was delighted.

"Come on, then," she ordered, and looked at her watch.

John asked Harriet if she were ready, and Harriet called another salesgirl. "I have to be off the floor a few minutes," she said, "take over for me, will you?"

Harriet came out from behind the counter and the four of us walked away, I a little behind the other three because I didn't know where we were going. The Victrola Department, I learned, was our destination. This was the first time I had seen it and I would not have guessed its location because no sound of music was coming from it at the moment.

My three friends went up to the counter nearest the Book Section and asked the young man clerk there if they might try out some records. He said he'd be delighted to get for them whatever they wanted. John said he was particularly anxious to hear "The 1812 Overture," Ollie requested some Sousa marches, and Harriet was longing, she said, to try some John McCormack records.

While the young man was getting these from stock, John walked nervously back and forth, muttering he hoped they hadn't shaved it too close. It was obvious Ollie and Harriet were on edge too. They kept looking across into the Book Section, separated from where we were standing by only the width of an aisle. Just as the young man returned with the stack of records, I heard John Sheeley say, "Thank God, he's just coming now." I turned to follow the direction in which he was looking and saw Mr. Yates, the Vice-President of Marshall Field's, step out of an elevator a short distance from us and move in the direction of Marcella's office.

Immediately Ollie, Harriet and John snatched up a pile of records from the counter, to the young man's bewilderment.

"I don't think you've got the ones you requested. I haven't sorted them yet," he protested.

"That's all right," Ollie told him hastily. "We're all interested in these. We can shift them around ourselves."

There were four glass-enclosed booths along the boundary line between the Victrola and the Book Sections. My group headed for them. The young man followed, protesting again, and increasingly bewildered. "Those aren't our best booths," he said. "You get some noise from the elevators there. We have others in the middle of the section I'm sure you'd find much better."

My friends waved him off peremptorily, murmuring something to the effect that these were more convenient, they didn't mind, and they hadn't much time.

Ollie stepped into the one nearest her and said from the doorway to the clerk, "Don't bother waiting around, we don't want to keep you from other customers. We'll let you know what we select." Her tone was of command rather than request, and the clerk obeyed it. After hesitating only a minute, he turned and walked away.

Harriet and John darted into the booths beyond Ollie's. I stood outside them, wondering what was coming next. What came next, and almost instantaneously, was a volume of sound that rocked me where I stood, and simultaneously into my range of vision walked Marcella, her arm slid through that of Mr. Yates.

In a moment of exquisite timing, she drew him to a standstill in front of a table of books, as from the open doors of three booths ricocheted to them and back the combined strains of "The Stars and Stripes Forever," "The 1812 Overture" at its climax, and the piercing, lusty tones of John McCormack reaching his highest notes.

I saw Mr. Yates shake his head and then cup one hand around his ear. I saw Marcella smile gently at him and shake her head wistfully, then stand on tiptoe, putting her face close to his ear. After a minute or two she drew him gently away toward the center aisle. I followed shamelessly and as fast as I could make it.

I caught up with them and hovered near by in time to hear her

[ 208 ]

say, "I'm so terribly sorry, Mr. Yates, to take even more of your time than I asked for. I wanted your advice about a rearrangement of our Juvenile Department and our magazine subscriptions, you have such a wonderful flair for display. We weren't getting out of ours all that we might, I thought. I didn't mean to have to repeat this over to you, but we find we have to do everything twice now that the Victrola Department is next door. We can't wait on customers there any more. We have to take them into the center of the section to find out what books they were trying to ask us for. Of course, if they're in a hurry they won't be bothered and simply go away. But never mind about that. I don't want to trouble you with it; we'll make up our sales elsewhere. What I did so want to ask you was your advice."

"Why, Mrs. Hahner," I heard him say before I leaped back to my friends, "this is an outrage."

"It's all over," I shouted into each booth.

They shut off the music and came out to join me. Together we watched Marcella say good-by to Mr. Yates in front of the elevator. He patted her hand, a little soothing tap before he stepped into the waiting car, and she smiled after him until he was out of sight. Then she trotted back toward her office.

We strolled to Harriet's counter. Harriet looked back once over her shoulder in the direction of the Victrola Section. "I give it about a week," she said.

She was wrong. The Victrola Section was moved out over the week end, just three days after the concert.

## * 14 *

ONE OF the surprising things I learned at Field's was the paradox that things and people never seemed to change and would change overnight. Clerks worked in the same sections for fifty years; the way of advertising, the way of displaying merchandise, went round and round without variation. And staggering transformations could occur in the store without warning.

Our group in the Advertising Bureau talked about this frequently at lunch. Some aspect of this policy, we felt, was always blocking an idea one of us had had; an idea that if carried out would have brought customers running to the store by the thousands, huzzaing as they ran. This was denied them by the exasperating store management that would not move faster than a glacier, and contrariwise just as you'd got one executive at least to listen to your ideas and had a faint hope of getting him to do something about them, he'd suddenly be changed over to manage departments quite different from those he'd had under his command when you were working on him.

Our group had lost some and added other members since I'd been taken into it. Margaret Haggett and Buff Corse had gone to New York and were deeply missed. Mrs. Hill, who came from St. Paul, was the successor as head of the newspaper advertising. Bessie Zaban and Helen Sisson were recruits placed under her, and Katherine Gardner, not related to Achsah, but the heir, in wit and gaiety, to Buff Corse. In addition to Helen Wells, Frances McFadden had been taken on the staff of *Fashions of the Hour*. In spite of strong protesting cries from her mother, Frances had been determined to have a job, and had come to Field's, having heard it was the home in Chicago for such wayward girls.

Immediately she was admitted she had ideas, not only about *Fashions of the Hour* or the newspaper advertising that was not our province, but all merchandising: buying, selling, displaying.

Placing Frances in Marshall Field's was much the same as setting a popper filled with corn over a flame. Almost the only difference was that there was no wire basket around her, and so her ideas popped in every direction. They were not all of them feasible, but none of them were stale. Achsah picked them up wherever they fell and filed them, teaching Frances, as she was teaching me, to work with and through an organization. And Achsah, sorting out the ideas that seemed possible, would evolve a presentation of them through the proper channels to the person who could authorize their being carried out, then refer the accomplishment and the credit back to Frances.

Pamela Coyne joined our group because I brought her into the Advertising Bureau. We had been at college together, she younger and in a lower class. We had met again when she was on a visit in Chicago. She had asked what I was doing and on learning had wanted to know if I thought she could possibly get a job at Field's too. Field's were taking us in, I had assured her, making an experiment of girls like us.

She was accepted, but with her arrival the management thought up and put into effect some new rules for us guinea pigs. Everyone joining the Advertising staff, it decreed, must go through an apprenticeship in the store proper to learn something about merchandising firsthand. It was an excellent idea, the rest of us agreed, and were profoundly thankful we had got in under the

wire before it was carried out. We followed Pamela's apprenticeship, however, with enthusiastic interest.

Her first assignment was as guide to sightseeing tours through
the store. This was preceded by an intensive instruction course.
Since none of us had been given that course, we felt an obligation
to learn from her. Accordingly, any of us in the Advertising
Bureau with a little free time on our hands would dress like customers in hat, coat, gloves, etcetera, and join her train. We always
asked more questions than any of the other sightseers, and we
were gratifyingly successful in thinking up questions not answered in her handbook of statistics about the store. She could
not dismiss us from the party, but we, in turn, could not ruffle her
Olympian composure beyond a blush. We even grudgingly admitted among ourselves that her answers to our cunning requests
for knowledge touched at times a peak of ingenuity.

When her term as girl-guide was completed we helped her
in our own way at her next assignment as salesgirl in the Toy
Department. Our purpose was not to purchase toys but to acquire
knowledge of the Toy Department, preferably at a time when she
was engaged with a customer. Her splendid response to this as a
loyal store employee was to send and charge to one of us, no
matter what the size or cost, the merchandise she was at the
moment of interruption displaying to a customer.

Shortly after adopting this method of satisfying our interest
she was transferred to the Fur Department and this brought
about a waning of interest on the part of her well-wishers from
the Advertising Bureau.

But when she returned to us, graduated from a school we had
never attended, we welcomed her enthusiastically and with respect. She was assigned to the newspaper and in a very short
time had, with Mrs. Hill, established an orderly routine that
could be and occasionally was performed quietly; certainly a contrast to the vociferous bedlam I had heretofore associated with
getting out an ad.

One morning we arrived at the Bureau to find the staff increased by the introduction of a gentleman named Tommy Thompson, whose function as a type expert was to be, Mr. Schaeffer explained, "a liaison officer" between us and printers. We had not known we needed liaison work, but we welcomed Mr. Thompson. That same day Hal Noble, who was a member of the Bureau when I joined it, was jumped from House Furnishings to head of all basement advertising, and Olin Stansbury moved from that post to the awesome dignity of Assistant Advertising Manager. We lesser wage earners greeted these unexpected leaps with jeers, congratulations, and a lunch in their honor. Even a minor change in the status of any one of us could make an occasion for a special lunch.

Whenever I had a bout with the timekeeper—I had one frequently—and came out of it the winner, I gave a lunch to celebrate, thereby eating up what I had wrung from the firm. The day I waved in the face of that enemy of the Bureau a note signed by an executive, that authorized the permanent exemption of the Advertising staff from punching the time clock, we had a lunch that lasted two hours, at our favorite Italian restaurant. On our return we all punched the time clock simultaneously and for the last time.

Members of the group lunched together anyway on an average of three or four times a week. We admitted to one another that engagements with old friends outside the store had become irksome. We weren't interested in their talk any more, and we fretted over the store talk we were missing. Our closed society and the store absorbed us. We discussed what brilliant things we would do if the old fuddy-duddies in charge would give us half a chance; we deplored their backwardness and reluctance to accept progress; we pooled the tidbits of gossip we had gleaned from our friends in the sections, and allowed ourselves to betray a little the superiority we felt over the people outside—because they came into the store merely to buy, but knew nothing of the world it constituted and that we were helping to run.

We came back from lunch one day, four or five of us, intending to go straight to Achsah's office to take up with her a discussion that had carried us through the meal, and that she had instigated. We'd been standing around at noon, waiting for Pamela to OK a proof, when Achsah had quoted something Mr. Corley, the General Manager, had said that morning. They had been talking about someone Mr. Corley contemplated letting out of the organization and Achsah had told him, dismayed, "Why, Mr. Corley, you can't discharge her. Don't you realize how clever she is?"

Mr. Corley's answer had been, "Miss Gardner, don't you realize this organization isn't built on cleverness?"

At the last minute Achsah had been called back to her office by Mr. Schaeffer and had told us to go on ahead, she'd join us if she could. She hadn't come and we had spent a good part of the lunch hour arguing about the importance of being clever. We wanted a few ideas from her on the subject before we separated.

But at the gate Albert had a message for me: Miss Gardner and Mr. Schaeffer were waiting for me in Mr. Corley's office. That shook us, but especially me, to such an extent that my friends, noticing, said, "Don't take it too hard," and "You haven't been stealing merchandise, have you?" and "The worst that can happen is to get fired, or can they jail you for what you've done?"

None of this seemed worth the effort to answer. I left them and walked along the passage to Mr. Corley's office. The young man I had come to know by now, the one who had taken me for an interview into Mr. Simpson's office, was at his desk and on the lookout for me. "Are you scared again?" he asked, and I nodded. "Well, don't be," he said. "You ought to get over it by now. Go on in. Mr. Corley wants to see you."

Mr. Corley, a vice-president and the merchandise manager, Mr. Schaeffer and Achsah were talking as I came in, but they stopped when I crossed the threshold and let me walk the length of the room in silence. I stopped in front of Mr. Corley's desk, because I didn't know where else to go, and he spoke. "How do you do, Miss Kimbrough?" he said. "These folks," indicating Mr. Schaeffer and Achsah, "have just been telling me they'd like to see you take over running *Fashions of the Hour,* because Miss Gardner is going down to the sixth floor to be style co-ordinator over all our Apparel Sections. We'd like this to be done immediately. Will it be satisfactory to you?"

In Achsah's office some time later I upbraided her for not having given me some warning of this upheaval. "People have fallen down dead," I accused her, "from a lesser shock than I had at Mr. Corley's desk." I was still shaking like a leaf on a poplar tree. Achsah was indignant. She'd only known about it herself, she protested, after we'd gone without her to lunch. Mr. Schaeffer had taken her in to Mr. Corley and they'd been talking about the shift and the rearrangement from then on until I'd returned.

She grinned a little sheepishly. "I was fresh to Corley, too," she said musingly.

I wanted to know what she'd said.

"Well," she told me, "first of all I suggested if I were to take over this other job I wanted considerably more salary. And I named a figure. Corley whistled at it and informed me he felt I held my services pretty high. That's when I got fresh. I said, 'Marshall Field's has taught me the value of quality.'"

"I guess that fixed him," I broke in.

"Not a bit of it," Achsah answered. "He came back quick as a flash. 'Then, Miss Gardner, it has taught you a very valuable thing.' And he wrote out an order to the paymaster for the raise."

I left Achsah's office and went to a public telephone booth in the Household Utilities Department. I wanted to tell mother without being overheard.

The shock seemed to be even greater to her than it had been to me. From the silence at the other end of the wire after I'd made my announcement, I thought she had fainted. I began yelling into the instrument, "Are you all right?" with a volume and a confused hope I might make myself heard past mother by the maid.

Mother overrode my clamor suddenly with a stentorian request. "Quiet!" When I had subsided she went on to explain she hadn't fainted, but had momentarily been stunned into breathlessness. She was, she added, overwhelmingly pleased and excited for me, but at the same time shocked at Marshall Field & Company. How could they possibly feel I was ready to take over the running of the magazine?

I found myself hotly defending Field's policy of entrusting responsibility to an individual. That was the way they built people, and after all, I said, the organization was so much stronger than the individual, it would automatically act as a check and a guide.

Mother conceded this might be so and added again I must know that, as far as I myself was concerned, she was jubilantly pleased, and it rested with me to remove any doubts she might have had. That was the end of our conversation.

Walking back to the Advertising Bureau I mulled it over and came to the conclusion I had not got from it the wholehearted praise I had anticipated. With a pleasant flutter of anticipation I went to the newspaper office to tell the news to my pals there, and get from them, I was sure, a tumultuous endorsement of Field's selection.

The girls were gratifyingly tumultuous, but there was more of an element of surprise than I cared for. I could also have done without the comment on the part of one of them that making me the Editor of *Fashions* certainly bore out what we had been talking about at lunch: that the Field organization was not built on cleverness and clever people. The rest of my gang received this observation with such gleeful enthusiasm they went to Harry Rodman, the Art Director, and got him to letter this slogan on a

large piece of cardboard. I learned they had done this when I moved next day into what had been Achsah's office, and found the card tacked on the wall above my desk: "Marshall Field's is *not* built on cleverness." Below this was a large vase of flowers. The combination was typical of the way in which my news was received by everyone to whom I told it, starting with mother. I might have got something better from Marcella, but she was, I knew, in New York. So I couldn't even tell her.

When I reached home after work the day of the big news, I found father there ahead of me, waiting impatiently to hear what had happened, because mother had said only that I would have something to tell him when I got home. She had not wanted to spoil my pleasure in making my own announcement. I could have wished she had spared me, because my announcement did not bring me undiluted pleasure.

It sent father into a state of shock almost the equivalent of mother's earlier in the day. I told my parents I'd been nearly knocked off my feet myself when told of my advancement, but if I'd thought that had been my prerogative and that other people, particularly my nearest and dearest, might have considered it in the light of a promotion due me, I had certainly been profoundly mistaken. I added the hope that no one would write my brother at boarding school about the event; judging from the effect on my parents, the announcement might send him to the infirmary.

Father asked me to put in a call at once to my Grandmother and Grandfather Kimbrough in Muncie, Indiana, and I went to the telephone happily. Grandfather was the patriarch of the family in the literal sense of being the head of it. Not one of his three sons nor any member of their families would have dreamed of allowing any family event to pass by without grandfather's being informed of it. My father telephoned him every Sunday morning to report on our welfare and our activities during the week; therefore it was a matter of course that I should inform him immediately of an unusual occurrence in my life.

I reflected contentedly, as I gave my call to the operator, that both my grandparents doted on me. I would hear from them the cries of pure happiness and pleasure my ear had not as yet picked up elsewhere.

They were both at home; grandmother as usual instructed me not to say anything until she should have gone upstairs to listen on the extension in her room. When she had established herself there, she said, "Now, Emily, what is it?"

I told them. "Today," I said, "I was made the Editor of *Fashions of the Hour.*"

They simultaneously requested me to repeat what I had just said. I repeated it.

"Why, that's fine, just fine," grandfather boomed heartily.

This was what I had been waiting for and I would have liked to hear it over and over again but grandmother's voice came cutting through, "Wait a minute, Charles," she said, "I want to ask Emily something."

Grandfather subsided.

"Now, dear," she went on briskly, "just what is it you do when you're the editor of a magazine?"

"Why . . ." I answered somewhat falteringly, because I was a little put to it to say concisely just what my job did mean in the way of work. "Why . . ." I repeated, "instead of just writing things for it, I will get out the whole magazine."

Grandmother interrupted with a loud noise of satisfaction, "Ah-hah," she said, "I was going to write you about this. I wanted you to tell me who could help, and you're the very one yourself. *I'm as pleased as I can be.* This is what I want you to do. When you're getting out the magazine, I want you to pay particular attention to the copy for Mrs. Eva Little. She hasn't been getting hers regularly lately, not since she gave them a forwarding address last summer. Now you know very well she's back home and her address is 614 East Washington Street."

The next day I moved my belongings from the desk in the outer pen to Achsah's office and helped her transpose her belongings, a considerably larger accumulation than mine, to her new quarters on the sixth floor.

On one of our trips I asked Achsah if she thought I might requisition through the management a private wire from her new office to mine, because I expected to send out an urgent cry for help on an average of once an hour and wanted no busy signal to get in my way. Achsah flouted the suggestion. I certainly ought to know by now the pattern for *Fashions of the Hour* and the over-all policy of the Advertising Bureau. Furthermore, Field's didn't like people running for help, she reminded me. They set you up in a job, they trusted you and they let you alone; something to be eternally grateful for. But they did not like leaners. Besides, she added, she expected to be fully occupied getting into her own new job.

When the last armload had been deposited in her office, I said good-by to her almost as if I were leaving on a train for a destination some miles away; because one of the curious aspects of the store was that though it made up an over-all world of its own, it was so subdivided, geographically and socially, that the sixth floor was inflexibly on the Apparel stratum, and we on the ninth floor, except for my friendship with Mrs. Hahner, an exclusively Advertising circle.

Achsah had been right when she'd insisted I knew thoroughly the pattern of *Fashions of the Hour* and of the Advertising Bureau. That basic knowledge was an integral part of the training given to everyone who came into the Bureau. It was not a secret operation controlled by Mr. Schaeffer, the Advertising head, with only the details of operation delegated to people on the staff. The entire staff participated in the initial plan and in every step from there to its execution.

The advertising budget for each department in the store was made up for a year, but before those figures were established, Mr. Schaeffer had discussed with us the appropriations to be allotted. And each staff member had, in turn, gone over the proposed budget with the Buyers of the sections represented in Advertising by that staff member. Mr. Schaeffer took the results of these discussions and suggestions to the management for the final allotments.

That appropriation was then broken down into months. *Fashions of the Hour* was concerned in this. We decided in which issue a section would be represented and how much space it merited according to its volume of business and its over-all appropriation. After that, the copywriters, each one representing a group of departments, would work out what days and in what papers the advertisements for each of those departments were to be placed.

This breakdown was synonymous with trouble. All Buyers clung to the same idea, a simple idea and unchanging—a full page in the Chicago *Tribune*. Even when they had been coaxed away from that idyll, they would almost every one of them come rushing up to the Bureau as the end of the month grew near, demanding a big spread, their only hope, they would protest, of beating a particularly big day of the corresponding month the preceding year, or because the entire month was going to fall into the red, and only a big spread could rescue it.

The invariable answer to this—it was the habitual end-of-the-month slogan from the Bureau: "Why, you haven't enough money left for an ad in the *Abend Post*." The *Abend Post* was a wistful little local German paper. Actually, the appropriation for specific merchandising was less at Field's than at other stores, but we had a larger budget than others for institutional advertising.

The Buyers were chronically provoked at *Fashions of the Hour* as well as at the newspaper staff. The cause of their displeasure was not at the space allotted but the way it was handled. In addition to these battles we carried on a civil war that occasionally slackened, but never ceased.

The civil war was the struggle between the Editorial and the Art Departments. The purpose of the magazine was to present the scope of Marshall Field & Company; its importance as a store and as a great institution in Chicago. It was called a prestige publication and the management instructed us to stress institutional advertising. Therefore, we ran articles about Chicago, or about almost everything if the writer were a well-known author. We gathered in a list of distinguished contributors partly through Marcella's coercion of authors after she became a friend of the magazine's, and partly by paying an author the same rate other publications offered.

We also went beyond the local group for our drawings. Most of our covers were done by French artists, commissioned through our Paris office, and many of our fashion drawings. The artists selected would accompany a Marshall Field Buyer to the Paris openings and sketch the models selected. The big dressmaking houses were usually chary about admitting artists, protecting fiercely their exclusive designs from the danger of copies made and sold. But they made an exception for Field's. The reason for this was that Field Buyers bought more than any others and also had greater freedom. Their selections and the amount they spent did not have to be endorsed by the management at home. The Field representatives went to an opening, made a wide selection of models, placed an order for these immediately and the transaction was completed.

Marty drew for us and Guy Arnoux, Martin, Helène Perdriat, Dupas and Boutet de Monvel. Most of the Buyers looked with a jaundiced eye on these and the distinguished modern American artists whose work we used. Their criterion of artistic excellence was that every button be included, and trimming shown with precise detail. Drawings for the newspapers had pretty much to fall in line with this, but on *Fashions of the Hour* we not only

[ 223 ]

had a free hand but encouragement to display on its pages what was new, what was original and, in our opinion, distinguished.

The presentation to a Buyer of one of these distinguished pages, and a request of an OK from her on merchandise illustrated and written about there, frequently brought from her an instantaneous response similar to that of a Frenchman whose face has been slapped with a glove. She would immediately call for seconds, and her assistants would come to her on the gallop. We would then call for ours, and a duel would be fought on the instant. And yet the Buyers never won so much as a decision, because our seconds were the management. And though the management sometimes quailed at the sight of a very modern drawing agitated in front of the eyes of the executives by a trembling Buyer dedicated at the moment to mayhem, it had put its hopes for prestige on the magazine, the responsibility on us; and it upheld both.

The war between our Editorial and Art Departments was more evenly balanced, almost equally fierce. Each time an issue was being put together, the Editorial Department accused the Art Director of creating layouts that were all artwork and left no room whatever for copy. The Art Department parried with the assertion that a vivid and striking illustration had far more value than anything one could write about the subject. If the Editorial Department complained that a hand-lettered title was impossible to read, the Art Department answered that it made, nevertheless, a charming design.

These were major issues, but petty skirmishes could be counted upon to result from an aggravating habit, practiced by the Art Department, of submitting to the Editorial Department new drawings to be passed on by spreading them about on the floor. This necessitated moving chairs out of the way and hunching down awkwardly in order to view what was being submitted. But all protests that pictures in Art galleries were not thrown on the floor were met by the lofty assurance that the only way

[ 224 ]

properly to estimate the value of a composition, was by looking down on it.

The Art Director of *Fashions of the Hour* was a brilliant and a determined woman, with a flair close to genius for discovering and developing talent in young artists. She created techniques that had never before been used in fashion drawing, and taught them to the young local painters who worked for us. Neither the newspaper nor *Fashions of the Hour* included artists on its staff at a weekly salary. All the artwork was on a free-lance basis to insure variety and freshness, but a few of these contributors did such outstanding work as to overcome our policy of variety, and received enough commissions to make working for Field's a full-time job. Therefore, we had exclusively their total output.

One of these was the artist, Gladys Rockmore Davis, who was fifteen years old when she started to work for the magazine under the guidance of our Art Director. The Christys, man and wife—Wynne for design, and Dorothy with her enchanting drawings of children—were in nearly every issue of *Fashions of the Hour*.

Everyone who worked for our Art Director increased his artistic stature. They chafed under her rigid exactions but acknowledged that because of them better drawings were produced than the artist had previously achieved.

This was the over-all pattern of *Fashions of the Hour*, and under Achsah's teaching I had come to know it well. But taking over the running of the magazine involved watching over the ramifications of that pattern and coping with unexpected deviations from it.

One of the expected and inevitable ramifications with which to cope involved the Art Director's standard of perfection from a drawing through the completed plate or engraving. She operated on the principle that if a thing were done and redone enough times perfection would eventually be achieved. Each time an issue of the magazine was being got ready for the press, she put this theory to the test.

Time after time after time, engraving proofs arriving for her OK would be sent back to the printer with, instead, her scathing and marginal indications of their imperfections. And at each issue, members of the engraving department at the printer's came perilously close to a condition that puts its victims in state institutions behind bars; but at the same time they gave to the magazine reproductions of a quality that had never before been achieved. The perfection the Art Director saw in her dreams, however, was never fulfilled because there came a time when someone had to call "Halt" or something to that effect in order that the magazine might be locked for press and the issue published.

The person who said "Halt" was the Editor. The day I walked from my office into the Art Department and quavered, "These proofs have to be marked final; we'll go to the printer's tonight," I thought I had crossed the most difficult Rubicon becoming *Fashions of the Hour* Editor could present.

I was mistaken. My news was received by the Art Department with tolerant acquiescence. We went to the printer's that night, and in the early hours of the morning saw the issue into the lockup.

Back in the store the next morning, I had a message that Mr. Corley wished to see me in his office. The young man at the desk outside the Executive Offices looked up at my approach. "Mr. Corley wants to see me," I told him.

He smiled. "I know," he said, "and thank goodness you look a little less scared each time you come here."

"I really don't feel scared," I told him airily, and went on into Mr. Corley's office.

Mr. Corley was writing at his desk when I came in. He looked up briefly. "Sit down, Miss Kimbrough, will you? I'll be with you in a minute."

I sat down in the chair indicated beside his desk and waited. A few minutes later, without looking up, and still writing, or what seemed to be checking some kind of invoice, he said, "I don't know whether you know it or not, but your Art Director is pregnant. I'd like you to talk with her and find out how long she thinks she can continue working. If she's planning to quit her job you'd better be sure her assistant is ready to take over. Also, she's down on the payroll as Miss. We'll have to find out if she's married. We don't want any trouble around here."

If he wanted an immediate answer from me he was disappointed. Muscular and vocal paralysis had possession of me. I was unable even to think clearly. But the idea did race wildly around my mind that this commission was certainly not included in the over-all pattern of running *Fashions of the Hour* that Achsah had assured me I knew so well.

I certainly did not know our Art Director was pregnant though we had lunched and even sat through many nights together at the printer's getting out the magazine. She had not told me, either, that she was married. I had found her interesting and friendly, but reticent. I had not felt it any of my business to probe, however delicately, below that reticence. Now I had orders from an executive himself to probe with pick and shovel.

Mr. Corley came to the bottom of the page and looked up. "Well?" he asked.

"Are you sure she's pregnant?" I entreated, plucking, like Watt's picture of Hope, the lone string on a harp.

He nodded confidently. "No question about it. You can tell from the back of her neck. Always shows there first. Thickens up. I learned that from my years in the Millinery Section standing behind a woman trying on a hat. She's pregnant all right. Just straighten the matter out and send me word."

The interview was evidently over and I got to my feet. "Yes, Mr. Corley," I said and went out of his office.

The young man at the outer desk looked up at me as I passed him and his jaw dropped. "For Heaven's sake," he said, "after I

[ 227 ]

thought you'd got over being scared. You look really shot this time."

"I am," I told him, "but it's going to be worse," and went back to my office. I sat at my desk a long time, trying to work out a combination of words that would make a tactful way of saying to a reticent woman, "Are you pregnant, and are you married?"

Two or three of my pals passing by looked in the door and asked if anything were the matter, but I waved them off. "I'm having a page," I said, standard phrase in the Bureau for being left alone.

Several times I put my hand on the telephone to call Achsah for help, but each time thought better of it, remembering her request for me to do my own job. Finally I rang the Art Director and asked if she would lunch with me. She would be delighted, she said.

I took her to an expensive restaurant, paid for both of us, and kept her forty-five minutes over our lunch hour without being able to introduce the subject.

When we parted at the door of my office she thanked me warmly but protested I shouldn't have celebrated my becoming Editor by giving her a blowout. It should have been the other way around.

Three or four times during the afternoon I went to the Art Department when I knew she was there alone, and each time was unable to get beyond the topic of pages for the next issue. On my last visit she confessed herself mystified by my rush. Heretofore, she pointed out, we had always allowed at least a week after putting one magazine on the press, for going around the store, getting a general over-all sense of the merchandise we wanted to feature, before settling down to planning specific pages.

I did not go back to her again during the afternoon.

We had some time earlier scheduled a photographing session for that night. A shipment of glass had just come in from Sweden and we wanted to get pictures of it while the collection was still intact. This would be prestige and institutional advertising. We would explain in the magazine to our readers that the specific pieces illustrated might not still be in stock at the time of publication. It was, however, indicative of the kind of rare merchandise Marshall Field & Company included.

The Art Director and I went together to an early supper. As we came out of the restaurant we found it had started to rain. Back in the store again, my companion asked what time I thought we'd be through photographing. I told her I was sure it would not be later than eleven o'clock. She said she wanted to make a telephone call and would join me in the Glass Department on the second floor. I met the photographer there, the Art Director joined us in a few minutes.

We finished a little after eleven and left the photographer packing up his paraphernalia. When the Art Director and I came out of the store I saw a car drawn up at the curb just in front of the entrance. She noticed it simultaneously and waved to the driver, quickening her steps. He got out of the car, and hurried around toward us. When he reached us he put his arm around her, kissed her. And she turned to me.

"This is my husband," she said. While I was wringing his hand, she continued brightly, "He's being awfully fussy about me. He says I can keep on working up to the end, but he insists on coming for me whenever I have to stay down at the store late." She looked at him fondly. "I'm going to have a baby," she added.

I made a few babbling sounds, unable to shape them into words. But they were evidently adequate, because the happy couple smiled, said good night, expressed their sorrow that I did not live in their direction so they could take me home, got into the car, he tucking her in carefully and closing the door before going around to the driver's seat. They moved off and I, grinning happily in the rain, stood watching them out of sight.

## * 15 *

PHOTOGRAPHS WERE becoming increasingly an important feature of *Fashions of the Hour*. We used them not only to illustrate merchandise but to link the store to what was going on in Chicago opera, and in the theater there. We made pictures of opera stars, actresses and actors, too.

In one issue Roland Young, playing in Chicago in *Beggar on Horseback*, provided the illustration for a page on merchandise from the store for men, Patricia Collinge a tea-gown, and Julia Hoyt a black velvet evening dress. Two young women from the South, excellent photographers, came to Chicago and set up a joint studio. We began using them and they taught me a whole new approach to photographing in the store. Richards-Frear was the brisk signature affixed to their work. But the ladies themselves were anything but brisk. They were languorous, helpless, appealing little women with a technique for preserving that helplessness, beautiful to see. They not only scarcely so much as picked up an electric light bulb themselves, but managed to gather around them from all parts of the store a group of porters who counted it a privilege to move furniture under the direction of the lady artists, or to hold light standards, all the things that heretofore I had executed. This was a radical change in photographing technique, though a local one. Another change, brought

[   230   ]

about almost inadvertently by Eugene Hutchinson, was to have, I venture to assert, a far-reaching influence.

We were making pictures one day in Mr. Hutchinson's studio, and had taken along by taxi and a Field delivery wagon, the accessories, in addition to the costumes, we thought necessary. The accessories included everything from garden bench and table to Spanish shawls for background draping, china and glass bowls, flowers, books, bookends, etcetera. Nearly all photography was under the influence of the Baron de Meyer school that set down as a first principle a very, very busy background. As much detail as was possible to insert was crowded behind and around the subject. Sometimes it was difficult to tell the subject from the surroundings.

The subject that day in Mr. Hutchinson's studio was a young actress named Frances Howard. When the photographs were finished and Miss Howard released, she went to a dressing room to change back into her own clothes. Mr. Hutchinson and I discussed other pages for the magazine. We decided we would like to use Miss Howard again. Mr. Hutchinson called her name. She stuck her head out between the curtains of the dressing room saying, "Calling me?"

Mr. Hutchinson and I gasped. She had pinned a towel around her face and tight at the back of her neck to keep her hair in place when she pulled her dress off over her head. We had always considered her a beautiful girl, but seeing her like that away from all context was like seeing a sculptured Greek head; the high cheekbones, the deep-set eyes, the exquisite contours of her face narrowing to a delicately rounded chin, had a breath-taking purity in their disembodiment. We stared at her a moment while she looked questioningly from one to the other of us.

Mr. Hutchinson spoke first. "Come on out here," he said almost gruffly, "don't take that towel thing off. Put a wrapper or something on, but don't get dressed."

"All right," she said goodhumoredly, and retired again behind the curtain.

Mr. Hutchinson broke into fevered activity; pulling out lights, rolling the camera around, giving orders to me where I was to hold the lamp.

When Frances joined us, we were ready, though I had not the faintest idea what Hutchinson intended to do. He photographed her against a dead white screen again and again, under every kind of lighting and seemingly from every possible angle.

She was utterly bewildered by this kind of portrait, but a docile subject, asking only if this was supposed to be advertising Marshall Field & Company towels, because if it was, she said, our customers were going to get a surprise: she'd taken her towel from a Pullman.

About a week later there appeared in a display case beside the entrance to the building in which Mr. Hutchinson had his studio a portrait photograph that drew crowds of people. It was not a head, just a face, like a beautifully chiseled mask set against a background that was no background, only blank white, as if this were the marble from which the face had been carved.

When Frances posed for us the following week, she wore clothes from Marshall Field & Company, but she was photographed against a flat, gray screen made for the purpose in our own workrooms. There was no table near by set with a bowl of flowers, books in bookends, china knickknacks, and over the screen itself there was not draped so much as the fringe of a Spanish shawl. For us the Baron de Meyer school of photography had closed permanently. But we lost our beautiful model. She went out to Hollywood and married Mr. Sam Goldwyn.

Still another change that eddied far beyond *Fashions of the Hour* came about by way of our Paris office. We had a cable one day from that branch telling us the French dressmaker, Jean Patou, was planning to visit this country, would visit Chicago under the guidance of Henry Sell. Marshall Field & Company might like to do something in the way of publicity about this.

Henry Sell had once worked at Marshall Field & Company and gone from there to New York to become Editor of *Harper's Bazaar*. I felt sure that, faithful to the old Marshall Field & Company tie, he would steer Monsieur Patou toward our emporium and I thought we should make an occasion of the call. We conjured up one plan after another only to discard them all, and finally Frances McFadden hit upon an idea that, presented to the management, rocked those executives. But under constant, steady persuasion, they regained their normal stance, and having regained it, gave full permission and a lavish sum for a party in honor of Monsieur Patou, hostessed by *Fashions of the Hour*, at a stylish Chicago club, the Casino, with invitations to the most stylish among the members of Field's Carriage Trade.

This was the first time, certainly at least in Chicago, a dressmaker had been guest of honor at a party for the *haute monde*, and the first time the store had entertained such a group socially, outside its own building, and as friends, not customers. The invitations were therefore sent out with some trepidation. The acceptances whirled back at us immediately in such a cloud they might have been swept in with a broom. The party was a gratifying success.

We had begun the personalizing of the artists who designed clothes, as Marcella, before us, had personalized authors.

The executives were pleased because, after Mr. Schaeffer had pointed it out to them, they saw the event as a step ahead in institutional advertising.

The *Fashions of the Hour* staff was a little tired when the event was over, because in such spare time as we'd had while planning and giving the party we'd got out another issue of the magazine. It did not occur to any of us to ask for extra people to help, and the management, I'm sure, would have been astonished at such a request. The party had come under the head of promotional work and public relations, and these in turn were divisions of Advertising. The people in the Advertising Bureau were expected to do all of these things. And we did them.

We did not give such homage as we had rendered Monsieur Patou to the Queen of Rumania when she visited Chicago. But when she came to the store she was given a spontaneous reception that surpassed in fervor any ceremony we could have conceived in the publicity department.

There was a Buyer on the first floor whom I did not know particularly well, but I had found comfort in his gentle, even meek, acquiescence to any presentation of his merchandise that I submitted to him. I had even wondered that having such quality he had been able to push past others to become head of his department. With the arrival in the city of the Queen of Rumania, a complete metamorphosis took place in this Buyer that bewildered even the people in his own section who knew him far better than I.

One of these told me about the change, beckoning to me one day as I was passing through. He led me to a far corner behind a display table before he spoke, and even then shook his head several times, as if he could scarcely himself believe what he was about to tell me. "We don't know what's got into him," he began, and jerked his head to indicate the Buyer, who was at that moment standing in the center aisle peering toward Charley's Door with the intentness of an Indian Scout on lookout duty.

"Who's he waiting for?" I asked.

"The Queen of Rumania," my informer answered in a tone of such sarcasm he might have been saying "Little Red Riding Hood." "It's a fact," he added. "Ever since the Queen came in town he's been like that. He's got his ears so peeled he can hear her motorcycle escort sirens even on Michigan Avenue, and he goes scampering out through the door right onto the street. Thinks maybe he'll see the procession go by. And have you seen the way he's got himself fixed up?"

I had to admit I hadn't been in the section recently.

"Well," the assistant elaborated, "he's bought himself a new suit. He's taken to wearing a flower in his buttonhole every day. And he even walks different—struts up and down as if he were leading a Shriners' parade or something."

I asked if my informer was sure the Queen of Rumania was the cause of all this.

"Certainly," he answered, "he told me so himself. He just says all his life he's wanted to see somebody royal but never thought he'd get a chance. Now he's made up his mind since a Queen has come to Chicago, she's bound to do what every other visitor here does, come to Marshall Field's, and he's going to be ready for it. Says if he's on hand when she comes in she might even speak to him, ask him the way to some department or something. And he'd remember it all his life. That's why he's out there practically every minute. He don't even go up to the lunchroom any more. He brings in sandwiches and eats them at his desk. And while he's back there he's got one of his salespeople posted in the aisle. I never saw the beat of it. And him, that's never got excited about anything before!"

The next morning at half-past eight as I passed Mr. Schaeffer's office on my way to mine, I saw my boss at his telephone and waved. He beckoned to me vigorously and I went in. He was listening impatiently, raising his eyebrows and opening his eyes wide to indicate to me he was getting a big story. He then broke in on it. "Yes, sir," he said, "I have it all. Thank you very much for letting us know. We'll be ready. We appreciate this. Good-by." And he hung up.

He hung up and simultaneously jumped from his chair. "The Queen of Rumania's on her way down to the store," he said moving rapidly past me.

I turned and followed him to get his instructions.

"That was her secretary. She wants to come early so there won't be any crowd. Get a photographer and hold her down on the first floor if you can, until I get word to you I've got the executives lined up to receive her." He disappeared through the door that led to the Executive Offices.

I didn't stop to take off my coat. I ran to the Art Department, stuck my head in the door, requesting a photographer immediately on the first floor wherever the Queen was to be found. I was on my way to look for her. I called in the news through the open door of the newspaper office and left the Bureau on the run.

As I came out of the center bank of elevators on the first floor I saw the Buyer his salesclerk and I had been discussing the preceding day. They were together, some distance away, facing me and looking toward Charley's Door.

One instant later I saw coming through the Randolph Street door behind them a small group of people, perhaps five or six in all. I stood still a second to make sure of what I saw before I acted. And I saw a young girl and a beautiful woman step out ahead of the other members of the group that closed in deferentially behind them. I knew then my hunch was right.

Queen Marie of Rumania and her daughter, Princess Ileana, had come to Marshall Field's and were advancing along the aisle behind the Buyer whose whole way of life had been changed by the news only that they were in the same city as he.

Short of breaking into a yell or a clattering run, I could not reach him first. I could not give warning.

So I took off at a walk as close to a run as I dared make it. I would have waved to attract his attention, but I was in full view of the royal party, and he completely engrossed in his conversation, totally unaware of me and the party coming up behind him.

The Queen was the first to catch his attention. Still behind him, she spoke in a deep, rich voice with an unmistakably European accent. "May I see, please," she said, "some of your beautiful things there?" pointing to a showcase.

I think the Buyer knew immediately to whom the voice belonged, because he stood perfectly motionless staring ahead of

With a gentle sigh, he slipped quietly down in a dead faint.

him at me for a perceptible lapse of time. Then he turned to look up, for he was a small man, into the face not two feet away from him of Her Majesty, Queen Marie of Rumania. And with a gentle sigh, he slipped quietly down across the floor at her feet in a dead faint.

When he returned an hour or so later from the First Aid Room, restored though still somewhat shaken, he found on his desk an autographed photograph, left for him by the Queen. But he never saw her again.

The Advertising Bureau was always informed immediately of anything out of the daily pattern that was occurring in the store. Sometimes the word came direct by telephone from a member of the department in which the occurrence was taking place, in the hope we could make a publicity story of it that would bring a mention of the store and the particular section in other than paid advertising space on a newspaper. Sometimes word came by the moccasin telegraph. The speed of this method of communication in a department store approaches the speed of a rocket. I never failed to marvel at the way news got around that vast building.

On the day a famous actor brought his friend to the Underwear Department—"Lanjeray," in store parlance—and purchased for her there a $500 nightgown, having her model several for him before a selection was made, I was out of my office and in the section not more than three feet away from the happy couple when the package was delivered over the counter. I was sorry to have to tell the Buyer, who was a good friend of mine, we could not send this charming incident to the newspapers, in spite of the opportunity it would give us to include the information that Marshall Field & Company carried nightgowns selling for $500 and more.

In the Bureau we decided also reluctantly not to reveal the provocative episode of the theft of a clock that weighed just under two hundred pounds. Once they had been convinced that such a sizable object had actually been carried away out of the building, the store detectives did a more than competent job of tracking it down. That part of the story would have brought only credit to the organization; but the clock was found in the apartment of a modest and very frail old gentleman, who, when asked how he had got it there, answered simply, "I was wearing my cap. When I wear that I'm invisible." There was, we agreed, no other explanation possible. But we did not release the story.

We withheld, too, the incident of a gentleman who visited a first floor department one day, leading an armadillo on a leash. While he was protesting to distracted floorwalkers, clerks and the head of the section, his right to be accompanied by a pet, a confederate cleaned the near-by counters of all merchandise. It was not recovered.

All these unreleased stories, however, were brought home to mother for our mutual enjoyment, and along with them an account of what was happening in the lives of my friends in the store. Father was not particularly interested, nor were my friends outside the store, but mother was as fascinated as I by the thousands of separate individual whorls that made up the pattern of an organization.

Mother despised petty gossip but was almost passionately interested in and concerned about people. She was reluctant at first, however, to meet my friends in the store, preferring to hear about them. Her reason, she explained vehemently to me, was that she considered it undignified for me to have a parent coming into my office as if I were still at school and she making a visit to inquire from my teacher how I was doing. But I was determined for her to meet some of the people about whom I had so much to tell, and I persuaded her to allow me to invite for lunch on one Friday a few of my friends in the Bureau. After that it became a weekly event. Mother always came in town on Fridays for the concert. We would meet in the tearoom at Field's for lunch, mother treating, and that was incentive enough in the

A gentleman visited a department leading an armadillo on a leash.

beginning for an eager acceptance, on the part of my friends, of her invitation. But it was not long before they began asking shamelessly if they might join us, confiding to me their enjoyment of my young and vivid parent, and proving this by protesting for a "Dutch treat" basis.

From the time I began to work at Field's mother established the practice of waiting in town after the Friday concert in order to drive me home in the Electric, picking up father as well en route. In the beginning she chose to drive round and round the block, pausing, when there was space, to talk to Charley until I came through his Door. But as she became reassured that her presence in the Bureau did not jeopardize my job, she would leave the Electric in Grant Park and come up to my office to wait until I could leave. In the interval between the end of the concert at four-thirty and the store's closing at half-past five, she occasionally shopped in the store if she had specific errands. Aimless shopping she described as a particularly exquisite form of torture to her. Under family pressure she would admit a little defiantly that this did reveal a marked inconsistency in her make-up. In an art gallery or museum she could remain on her feet when her dear ones were reeling to any spot where they could sit down, and yet after only a very few minutes of shopping she would declare an urgent necessity to leave.

When I was not busy in the interval between concert and store closing time, I would take her through the store to meet my Buyer and salespeople friends, and this she confessed she found not in the least tiring. These friends were most of them shy with her at first, but after they had talked to her a little while, one of them would invariably say later in the midst of a confidence to me, "Tell your mother about this and see what she thinks." On the other hand mother, once she had met them, never sought these people out again, pausing only for a few words if she happened to encounter one. That one at our next meeting would make a point of reporting, "I saw your mother the other day. We had a little chat," as if in some way the conversation had been memorable; and almost always would add, "She looks as if a breath of wind might blow her away," or "She oughtn't to cross Michigan Avenue alone when the breeze is off the Lake," and time and time again, a final comment, "But she's certainly full of ginger," or perhaps "But I bet you have a lot of fun with her."

Mother was very slight in build. Each year the family reaffirmed a resolution to hang out flags from the windows on the day she pushed her weight over her peak of ninety-eight to one hundred pounds. It was not entirely a joke that she tired easily, though she never admitted this weakness, and was incensed at any mention of her health. She was of such vigorous spirit, exciting to everyone within its range, like a thin, sharp flame, that we were, father and I and brother away at boarding school, oblivious most of the time of her diminishing range of activities and her increasing physical incapacity, as she meant us to be.

I knew she was at home a great deal but I attributed this, when I thought about it, to a preference over any other activity for being alone and for reading.

One Friday night in January I went to the opera with a group of friends. As I left, mother was sitting in front of a crystal radio set father had recently purchased. She removed the earphones when she saw me and said across me to father who was reading near by, "I consider this a symbol of the passage of time and the new generation. Our child, dressed in her best finery goes to the opera, her parents sit at home and listen to it by way of this machine. Hers is the genuine now, and ours the secondhand and spurious." She chuckled a little. "Emily," she said, "before you go would you mind bringing me that string of artificial pearls I bought at Field's the other day? It seems to me the appropriate accessory for listening to opera by this method."

This was the first time mother had consented to use the machine, and only because it had been announced in the paper that the opera was to be broadcast. Mother had greeted the arrival in the apartment of the instrument with a dour distrust and, when father turned it on, had urged him to open the window. "If the sound," she said, "seems to be coming in that way, I'll believe the process of radio is a little more normal."

As I left she called out, "Have a happy time, darling. The old folks at home will be listening too—in this peculiar way."

When I came home that night Achsah was waiting for me, to my astonishment. Mother had become suddenly ill, she explained, and been taken to the hospital; father had gone with her. Just before they left she had asked father to telephone Achsah to come out and stay with me.

I made ready to go at once to the hospital but father came in a very few minutes later before I had finished changing my clothes. Mother was critically ill, he said, but they had urged him not to stay lest that alarm her. We would both go early in the morning. Brother must be telephoned at boarding school in the East, to come home at once.

Outside the door of her room the next morning the surgeon and the family doctor, who was our dear friend, told father and me she would not live through the day. Father went away down the corridor with the two men and I went into mother's room. She was propped up against the pillows, her face sharp and white but her eyes as live and gay as they had always been.

"Emily," she said, with no preamble of why she was there nor how she felt, "I got to thinking early this morning about an approach of yours to reading that I frankly think is deplorable. I'm inclined to blame Bryn Mawr for it. I think you're so trained there to look for style, you ignore one of the most important achievements of writing, to tell a good story and to tell it well. I'm indignant at this current fashion of belittling Kipling. Kipling is a magnificent story-teller. So is Du Maurier. Have you ever read *Trilby?*"

Trying to meet her where she had always dwelt, in the mind, I managed to answer I had not read *Trilby*.

"Then get a copy," she said, "right now. Let's begin it."

The door opened at that minute and a nurse came in the door. "I'm going out for a few minutes," I said, "Mrs. Kimbrough wants a book."

The nurse's eyes widened, but she was turned away from the bed. Mother did not see her face.

I went out of the room and ran to the telephone booth at the end of the hall. I called Field's and got Marcella's office. "Marcella," I said, "mother's desperately ill but she wants to read *Trilby*. It's important. She's at Mercy Hospital. Can I get a copy?"

"Right away, dear," Marcella said and hung up the telephone.

In not more than twenty minutes a copy of *Trilby*, brought, as I learned later, in a taxi, was delivered to me.

Mother was pleased. "Now," she said settling into her pillows, "I wish I were going to have the treat that's in store for you, to read for the first time in your life the story of *Trilby*."

I began to read aloud. At twelve o'clock the Saturday noon whistles blew and I stopped reading until the noise should cease. Father had tiptoed into the room some time before and was sitting by the side of mother's bed, her hand in his. She smiled at me when I looked up. "Such good story-telling," she said and turned on the pillow to smile at father.

And then, at that instant a look of incredulous astonishment came over her face, and she died.

When I went back to the store a week later, Mr. Simpson sent for me. The young man at the outer desk smiled as I came through the gate, said he was glad to see me getting less scared each time I paid the Executive Offices a visit. He added Mr. Simpson was waiting for me, to go on in.

As I came through the door Mr. Simpson got up from his desk, shook hands with me and expressed his sympathy. I was not in the least surprised that he had learned about mother's death, knowing, as I did by now, that the executives had knowledge of almost everything about almost all of us in their organization. But I was surprised that he would concern himself personally about it and about me. I was even more surprised and touched by his thoughtfulness when he went on to say he'd sent for me to suggest I take a vacation from the magazine. As long as I wanted, he added; the job would be held for me, my salary would continue, I should come back only when I felt I really could take it on again.

I was totally unprepared for any such consideration and such a suggested program, and therefore totally unprepared to answer. But I found myself saying after a minute's hesitation something I had not until that instant known.

"Thank you more than I can say," I told him, "but please don't ask me to do that. Up to now this job has been fun. Now it's my base. I can't explain it very well," I went on fumblingly, "but I know that I need to work. Not just to fill in each day after what's happened, but because work is important to me. It's substantial. It's sustaining. I don't ever want to be without work again as long as I live."

# * 16 *

CLARA WILSON returned to Field's one day as unexpectedly as she had left. She had been Editor of *Fashions of the Hour* before my time and had left to become Art Director of *Harper's Bazaar*. That was what had brought Achsah from the newspaper advertising to take her place and provided me with a job, because with everyone's moving up one, there'd been room left at the bottom, into which I had squeezed.

And then one morning, when I was Editor of *Fashions of the Hour*, she'd come into my office, a tiny woman with large, shining black eyes. "I'm Clara Wilson," she said briskly, "I used to have your job. Now I've come back to organize and run the Interior Display in the store."

I'd scarcely got to my feet and said how glad I was to see her and that I knew all about her, when she was gone, darting into the other offices, as I could tell from the sounds; being vociferously welcomed by old friends and introduced to the people who had come in since her departure. There was not one of us who didn't know about her, because she was so frequently quoted. It was almost a routine comment when we were shown a particularly elaborate and preposterous import to repeat what she had once muttered under her breath, but audibly, on such an occasion, "Just the thing for a rainy morning on the El."

[ 248 ]

In the late summer, when merchandise from the Fancy Goods Section was submitted to us, hopefully, for inclusion in the Christmas Number, and we looked on much of it with indigestible disfavor, we were only echoing her sentiment that, "I enjoyed Christmas until I had to advertise night-light dolls."

I'd heard from Buyers, Mr. Bunker in the Linens especially, how ingenious she was in thinking up ways to link the store to the community; needlework lessons, lampshade-making, and in his section having socially prominent women come in to decorate tables as part of the January Linen Sales promotion; and how she had insisted these women be paid, to donate the money to their particular charity.

Immediately on her return Mrs. Wilson began to agitate for changes in the manner of displaying merchandise in the store. The vigor of the little woman was extraordinary. In the Advertising Bureau we knew of her agitation by a series of tremors that came to us daily from the Executive Offices, expressed on a seismograph of penciled notes sent in to Mr. Schaeffer and passed on to me. One of the first of these written by hand in a trembling script read: "Mrs. Wilson says, 'Brown paneling in the French Costume Room makes both merchandise and women look sallow.' Wants it covered with soft draperies. Doesn't seem to realize that paneling is solid mahogany."

Another complained tremulously, "Mrs. Wilson wants to light the display figures in the sections. Apparel Buyers say lighting will scorch the garments. Can you do something about this?"

Later that same day another plea arrived, scarcely legible but we made it out to read: "Mrs. W. wants canary birds in cages hung along the aisles in Household Utilities Department for Fall Exposition. Buyer has already consented to let her discuss with manufacturer making kitchen utensils and implements in color."

The day those particular notes came in was one I would not forget. It was the Saturday preceding the opening on Monday of the Fall Exposition, and that was, except for Christmas, the biggest over-all event in the store, with decorated windows to be revealed on Monday morning. The entire interior of the store was to be festooned with elaborate autumn trimming and every department glittering with individual display adornments of its new Fall merchandise.

On Monday the Advertising Department would herald the Exposition with a full-page fanfare in every paper. *Fashions of the Hour* had already gone to press and would be out on Monday to coincide with the opening. Our work was done, so we had been recruited to help the newspaper and the promotional people. Everyone in the Bureau had come down to work at eight o'clock, there was so much to be done. At eight-thirty the entire staff was gathered around the long table that ran the length of the outer office. We were correcting newspaper proofs, pasting up layouts on new ads, telephoning the newspaper last-minute changes, everyone working at top speed, when I was summoned to my office telephone. Because of the bedlam at the table outside, I could scarcely hear the little voice at the other end of the wire until I stuck my finger in the ear not shielded by the telephone receiver and made out it was Mrs. Wilson, asking in a voice not much above a whisper but with a quaver of urgency in it, if Mr. Schaeffer and I could meet her in the Fur Section immediately.

I hung up and went out to Mr. Schaeffer at the table, communicated the message to him, adding, "It sounds urgent." We looked at each other with a wild surmise and simultaneously set off on a trot for the Fur Section. Mrs. Wilson was waiting for us just inside the entrance to that department.

"I thought I'd better tell you," she explained, "what I had in mind before I show you what has happened."

The head of that department we knew had been the hardest to win over to Mrs. Wilson's ideas for a new kind of interior display. He had always bought from the basement, or coaxed from a Buyer without paying, faded dresses that could not be sold. He had put these on forms in his section and over them draped whatever fur he wished to display, from muskrat to chinchilla or sable. This had distressed Mrs. Wilson, and after a great deal of cajoling on her part she had persuaded him to allow her to put on something special for the Exposition.

She described this to us. In a big display case she had set up a winter scene. She and her assistant had worked until midnight the night before making it ready and had gone home well pleased with the result. They had left the display lighted so the sales-people, coming in the following morning, would be able to see it immediately in its full glory; then it would be shrouded until Monday. But she herself had come down a little early in order personally to reveal it to the Buyer.

The Buyer had not as yet come in, and for that, she assured us quaveringly, she was profoundly grateful, because something unusual had happened overnight to the display.

She led the way to the case, a very large one, able to hold a group of full-sized figures. Mr. Schaeffer and I could make out the figures only dimly, because the entire case was a swirling cloud of moths. The Buyer arrived while we were looking at this, and, after he had been revived, was so busy getting every garment in his section up to the Fur Storage Department for de-mothing before Monday, he wasted no time in conversation. Even without speech from him, however, it was apparent to the three of us that Mrs. Wilson was not going to find it easy to win back his co-operation.

It had not been difficult, once our eyes grew accustomed to the phenomenon, to see what had caused it. At the bottom of the case, moths were emerging from the artificial snow Mrs. Wilson had placed there in artistic mounds. She protested—and she was close to tears—she'd been given so little money to spend on the display, she'd shopped and bargained for every scrap of decoration she needed, and had been enormously pleased to get at a great bargain from the Window Decorating Department upstairs some cartons of artificial snow left over from Christmas windows several years previous.

Mr. Schaeffer and I returned to the Bureau and the newspaper ads. Around noon we had a telephone call for help from the Buyer of the Boys' Clothing Department. Arriving there, we discovered Mrs. Wilson shared honors for this crisis with a member of our own department. Our contributor, wrung with sympathy for the Buyer of Boys' Clothing, who, with a big day to beat and no money for advertising, had persuaded a magician appearing currently in a local vaudeville theater to put on in the section a demonstration of his art. She had promised him publicity and achieved it by an item in the day's ads, conspicuously boxed, announcing his appearance. This had cost the Buyer far less than an ad with cuts would have totaled.

Mrs. Wilson as the head of the Interior Display had been consulted on the most advantageous place for staging this performance, and she had designated a spot that would be most easily visible from all parts of the section. Pointing out that a large mirror already there would make an effective backdrop, she had installed a platform in front of it. She had not calculated, however, nor had our staff member, nor anyone in the Boys' Clothing Department, that the mirror would also reveal exactly how the magician did his tricks. The artist, intent on his work, had not even noticed the mirror. It was brought to his attention, however, and to the attention of every one in the section, when the crowd assembled. A stampede of little boys, with and without parents, had pointed out the flaw with hoots, jeers, catcalls, and, getting rapidly out of hand, had followed their vocal display by hurling at the misguided man who had wanted publicity every loose piece of merchandise within reach: shirts, socks, sweaters, and privately owned missiles from their own pants pockets.

When Mr. Schaeffer and I arrived, the magician had jumped

The mirror revealed how the magician did his tricks.

down from the platform and was cowering behind it, endeavoring to pack into his suitcase with trembling hands all his impedimenta. His counterattack as he huddled over the suitcase was verbal: a cascade of words delivered in a shrill, piercing voice without pause; all the words sub-Marshall Field & Company standard.

Mr. Schaeffer jumped on the platform and in his Rog-Old-Scamp voice, that could be heard all around and beyond the department, restored order by his hearty assurance this was the smartest bunch of young people he'd ever encountered, to guess so quickly the tricks of a magician; adding of course that it had been Marshall Field & Company's idea in the first place, not just to bring a magician, but to give its customers the added treat of letting them see how the tricks were done. So the customers could go away and, with a little practice, perhaps be able to do the same stunts themselves.

While this grandiloquent speech was going on, I was at the telephone behind a counter near by asking Mr. Cavenaugh, head of the Candy Section, to send us on the run several gross of lollipops charged to the poster account of the Advertising Bureau. Whenever we incurred an expense difficult to catalogue we put it under "posters." The management accepted this and did not seem to notice the discrepancy between a formidable sum apparently paid for posters and the very small number of actual posters throughout the store.

The lollipops arrived while the salespeople were restoring to their piles the sweaters, shirts and other implements of the recent barrage. Mr. Schaeffer was concluding his speech with the fervent assurance that no merchandise had been harmed, that Marshall Field & Company would not think of imposing any penalty for the disturbance in the section, and on the other hand was delighted to welcome these guests. And he, Mr. Schaeffer, felt personally sure the guests would like to remain in the section, show their appreciation for the performance and for Marshall

Field & Company's lack of resentment of the recent insurrection by asking the clerks to show them the special merchandise assembled for this particular occasion.

Hearty applause greeted the end of this speech. I distributed lollipops. When we left, the Buyer walked with us to the end of the section, beaming happily at the large number of customers that had remained and formed into line at various counters waiting to be served.

The staff was still working on proofs in the Bureau when we returned and we joined in once more. As we worked I was reminded by several members of the regular newspaper staff to let them double-check any copy I might write. This was an unkind reference to the only other occasion I had helped the newspaper people.

In June I had volunteered to help on a series of big ads featuring Commencement. It had been a rush job and since our Brides Number had just gone to press I'd offered my services to the newspaper. I'd written a block of copy on graduation dresses for little girls passing from elementary to high school. I had described a scene on the platform—the graduates in their crisp, white dresses from Marshall Field & Company—and I'd completed the picture in a final flurry of prose. "Facing the platform," were my words, "will be row upon row of expectant parents." Somehow this had escaped the notice even of Mr. Exley, but not of a great many readers who wrote Field's of their pleasure in the remarkable Commencement audience described in the advertisement.

After the third or fourth reminder of this I refused to have any more to do with copy, and allied myself with the Art Department to help paste up revised layouts. I went into my office for my own jar of rubber cement, and was just removing it from my desk when the telephone rang. The call was from Ollie in the Book Section, and it was a call for help. I said I would be right down and hung up.

I knew there was an autographing party scheduled at three-thirty in the Book Section. I'd been invited by Marcella to lunch with the distinguished poet who was to read some of his work and autograph copies of his latest volume. I'd had to refuse the invitation because, I'd explained, we were rushed getting ready for the Monday Fall Exposition opening. She had been a little annoyed by my refusal, I remembered as I started out of the office, but I felt that could hardly have brought on a crisis.

"Marcella's exploding," was the news I shared quietly with Mr. Schaeffer as I passed him at the table, "Ollie's sent for me."

Mr. Schaeffer blanched. "Even Field's," he muttered back to me, "can't take much more."

I signed out on the chart, "Section 86," and was on my way.

Ollie wasted no time in preambles. "It's the toilets," she said, "the place the boss decided for the stage is right up against the wall of the Rest Room. We never thought of it. The boss chose the place because we're expecting a big crowd this afternoon and she thought it was the best spot to be seen. But our poet, if you please, decided just now when they got back from their lunch party to sit down at the platform and try it out to see if everything suited him, lights and all. He no sooner got up there and sat down than he began to shout. You could hear him half-way down the section. 'Toilets! Toilets! Am I to read my poetry against the sound of flushing toilets? Flush! Flush! Roar! Roar! and a line of poetry. Flush! Flush! Roar! Roar! I can't have that, you know.' And that," Ollie concluded, "is the fix we're in. Can you think of anything to do?"

I asked where the visitor was at the moment.

"In the boss's office," was Ollie's answer, "with her. She's soothing him down by promising everything will be taken care of. And she's left word with me to have the platform moved. Well, we can't, that's all. Look at that setup. We'd have to take the platform apart and put it together again. We've got thousands of books stacked up. We've got plants around. We've got special lighting plugged in. Why, it took us to eleven o'clock last night to get the display arranged."

She looked around wildly. People were pouring into the section. "Listen," she said, "you go stop up those toilets somehow. I've got to stay here and handle this audience. I'll tell the boss that Rabbit Ears won't hear any toilets flushing, and I'll do something for you someday, see if I don't, if you help me out on this."

She left me in front of the elevator and hurried off toward her public.

By means of ten dollars I won the co-operation of the Rest Room attendant. She propped open the door to the outer waiting room. I posted myself in the doorway between the waiting room and the Book Section. From there, by standing on a chair, I could see over the crowd the poet at a desk on the platform. The Rest Room attendant and I were ready for him. Each time he started to read, I signaled to her and she barred the entrance to the Rest Room. The moment he stopped reading and began autographing volumes, I signaled again and my partner withdrew the barrier. The stampede that followed would have drowned out any reading if delivered through a megaphone, even without the subsequent "Flush! Flush! Roar! Roar!" But the instant the poet put down his pen and picked up his own volume saying, "Now I will read to you from—" I waved my arm and the barrier was up again.

The reading was a gratifying success. The poet himself assured me of this in Marcella's office where we had tea together. But I particularly treasured his parting remark when I said I must get back to my office. I had things to do, I apologized, before closing time. Holding my hand in his as we said good-by, the poet asked, "Do you not find it monotonous working in the confinement of an organization that has a set opening and closing hour every day?"

Reviewing hastily in my mind an average day, and this particular day about to close, I told him with deep sincerity I had not found working at Field's monotonous.

In the Bureau the tumult had died. The proofs had disappeared from the table. The staff was in its several offices, but in mine, the office boy told me, a gentleman was waiting to see me. I was surprised, and said so, that anyone should come so late.

"He's been waiting over two hours," was Albert's answer.

My caller stood up as I came into the room apologizing for having been away so long. He was a short, heavy-set man, and shy, because he said hesitantly and diffidently it was entirely his fault, at least he was his own cause for waiting because he had not written nor telephoned ahead to make an appointment.

When I had sat down at my desk he became silent as if he wanted me to say something. The only thing I wanted to say was that I was considerably annoyed at his being there, to assure him that if he'd put through the kind of day that was just ending for me, he'd want to go home too and not see anyone; just have a bath, and supper on a tray in bed. I could not think how to phrase these sentiments politely and so there was an interval of silence between us.

He finally broke it. "I'm from the *Ladies' Home Journal*," he said timidly.

This item of information I considered the final backbreaking straw of the day. At least four times a year somebody came from the *Ladies' Home Journal* Pattern Company to ask if I did not see my way clear to changing our editorial policy so as to include in the pages of *Fashions of the Hour* some *Ladies' Home Journal* patterns. And each time I said all over again that the *Fashions of the Hour* editorial policy was one fixed by Marshall Field & Company and not subject to change. No outside organization could advertise its name product in the pages of a Marshall Field & Company publication.

Hearing that name again at the end of such a day gave me an

[ 259 ]

irresistible urge to battle, and I responded to it generously. "Now see here," I began slowly and happily, "I don't ever want to see anybody from your organization again. Your office keeps sending one after another of you out here with the same old sales talk. But our answer doesn't change either, and I don't want to have to say it again. I'm sick to death of your people not being able to accept our word. No wonder you didn't write nor telephone for an appointment. You knew very well I wouldn't see you; I have nothing to say to you that I haven't said to all the other people. You can take this back for the last time; you're never going to hear it again because nobody they send is ever going to get in here again. *Fashions of the Hour* is not going to run *Ladies' Home Journal* patterns, or *McCall* patterns, or *Vogue* patterns, or anybody's patterns—ever. It's a Marshall Field & Company publication. And neither you nor anybody else can buy space in it. Have I made myself clear once and for all?"

My visitor cleared his throat. "You have indeed," he said quietly. "But I'm afraid I've not made myself quite clear. I have nothing whatever to do with the *Ladies' Home Journal* Pattern Company. I'm the Editor of the *Ladies' Home Journal*, and I have come out here to ask if you would consider coming to our organization as Fashion Editor of the magazine."

I hadn't since the age of thirteen felt myself blush as I felt the hot color mounting then. "I wish I were under my desk out of sight," I said faintly.

"That's all right," he answered reassuringly, "forget it. Everybody makes mistakes and I didn't help you any. I'm not very good at making myself clear when I start talking. I have to wind up a little." He smiled engagingly. "Now," he continued before I could break in to apologize further, "I want to ask you something else. You've been abroad for this magazine, haven't you?"

"Yes," I said, "and, believe me, I am terribly sorry to have been so rude. I had a full day before this happened."

He nodded.

And I continued. "Yes," I repeated, "I've been abroad for the magazine. The first time I went on a holiday trip really, with my father and brother, after my mother died. But I did work for *Fashions* on that trip both in Paris and in London. Since then I've made two trips for the magazine, working with Buyers and with artists."

"That's what I understood," my caller said. "And by the way, my name is Curry, Barton Curry. I know yours is Emily Kimbrough."

I felt it was a little late to acknowledge his introduction, though I would have liked to begin all over again. But I said nothing.

He continued. "The reason I wanted to verify your going abroad is that if you decide to come with us, as soon as you've got your department organized I'd like you to go abroad and set up a Paris office for the *Ladies' Home Journal.* Can you give me any idea now whether or not you would consider this job? Then if you would, we could meet again, perhaps tomorrow, to discuss details and terms. But you don't have to answer now. I'm staying at the Blackstone. Why don't you think it over and call me there tonight or tomorrow, if you can? I'd like to know, of course, as soon as possible, but I can wait."

Suddenly I thought of mother saying, "Every girl should be independent. I want my daughter to have a job," And, "With your shield or on it, Emily."

It had been four years, and over, since she had called that out to me on the morning I'd left the apartment to ask at Marshall Field's for a job from Achsah Gardner. Achsah was married to my father now. The two people whom I loved dearly making a life together. It was time for me to take up my shield again.

"You don't have to wait, Mr. Curry," I said, "I'll come."

# * L'Envoi *

IN JANUARY, 1951, I was writing this story and I wanted to spend some time in the store again; seeing such old friends as were still there, finding how the store had changed during the years, and sharpening my memory a little of how things had been when I had come through Charley's Door every morning at half-past eight.

I wrote the head of the Advertising Bureau asking if I might do this and received in reply a cordial invitation to come and to stay as long as I liked, adding that I would be given an office where I might talk conveniently and uninterruptedly to those friends with whom I wanted to reminisce. The office would be in Executives' Row. The executives had moved, the letter explained, from their old quarters. They now occupied an entire floor in the Store for Men Building.

On the morning I came down to Field's I stopped at the corner of Wabash Avenue and Washington Street waiting for the signals to change so that I could cross Wabash. I remembered how I had stood there the morning I was on my way to apply for a job, and how big the store had loomed across the street, and how frightened I'd been looking at it.

The policeman blew his whistle for the east-west traffic to move. The whistle hadn't changed; two notes that sounded like three because the second one dropped as it died away. "WHEE, whee-whee," my brother had imitated it. I remembered that as I stepped off the curb.

I stopped at Charley's Door for a minute for old time's sake. Charley wasn't there any more. He had died a few years before. A friend had written me that, adding that Charley at his death had been a prosperous and substantial citizen.

I crossed over to the Store for Men on the opposite side of Washington Street. An attractive young woman was waiting for me when I stepped out of the elevator. Asking if I were Miss Kimbrough, she told me she'd been assigned to help me gather the material I wanted and would show me my office.

On the way down a corridor she stopped at a door, opened it, disclosing a coatroom where she suggested I might like to leave my wraps. I took off my coat, gave it to her and she hung it on a hanger. I turned away and started on down the corridor.

She called after me, "Miss Kimbrough," and I turned back. "Don't you want to leave your hat?" she reminded me.

And out of a corner in the attic of my mind came my answer as quick and spontaneous as if I had spoken it only the day before. "No," I told her, "I want to go down through the store."

I had not thought since 1927 of the Marshall Field rule that decreed we in the Advertising Bureau must wear our hats when we went through the store, lest a customer mistake us for a sales-girl and be annoyed that we could not wait on her.

On the desk in my office I found a note that Mr. McBain would like to see me if it were convenient, as soon as I came in. My assistant dialed his office and spoke to his secretary, listened a minute or so, and hung up.

"Mr. McBain is terribly sorry," she reported, "but something unexpected had come up. He's had to postpone seeing you until this afternoon. If four-thirty isn't convenient to you, I'm to call his secretary back."

It would be convenient, I said.

"Would you like me to check with you about supplies you'll need?" she asked.

Suddenly I was excited. I was the old fire horse with the smell of smoke in his nostrils. I was in my store again, belonging there, and I wanted to see it all, as fast as I could cover it. Just as in the old days, the instant I'd reached my office in the morning, I'd wanted to get down through the sections immediately to find out what was going on.

"No," I said to my young helper, "never mind about supplies now. Will you dial Section Eighty-six for me and ask if I can come down to see Miss Oller, I mean Mrs. Harbaugh? We didn't have dials in my day," I added, "I don't know the number."

"Section Eighty-six?" she echoed politely, but in bewilderment.

"Yes," I told her. "The Book Section."

At her look of surprise I burst out involuntarily.

"It's coming back in such a rush," I confided, "as if I'd never been away. Eighty-six is Books, and Twenty-two is China, and Twenty-eight is the Custom Apparel Section. It's called that because the address over the Washington Street door, Charley's Door, the stylish door, is 28 Washington Street." I checked myself and apologized for what, I told her, must seem to her like a touch of gabbling senility.

She assured me courteously this was not so, but I did not risk further revelations to her.

Mrs. Harbaugh, the message came back, would see me as soon as I could get down there.

I went over to the Main Store by way of the passage under Washington Street that brought me out in the basement. But I went as unerringly as a sleepwalker, and in something of that same trance, to the bank of elevators that would bring me directly out at the Book Section.

Ollie was in her office and Harriet Smith with her. We'd seen one another at intervals during the intervening years, but somehow this meeting was different. I belonged again.

Almost immediately we talked of Marcella, who was dead. Ollie was head of the section but had never moved into Marcella's office.

"I somehow never wanted to," was her explanation. A few minutes later she said, "Do you remember how Marcella always used to tell us the day she found she'd grossed a million that year she'd resign, or maybe die?"

Harriet and I remembered.

"Well," Ollie continued, "did you know that one year after she died the section grossed a million? I felt just awful."

Harriet broke in. "You know what she did? She celebrated by crying her heart out."

"It was salt in my mouth," Ollie said.

We talked about other things. I told them I had an office in the Executives' Row and an assistant. They remembered the first office I'd had, a desk in a pen with the typists who worked for the executives.

"You know who'd get the biggest bang out of that, don't you?" Harriet interrupted. "The little boss. She'd laugh herself sick to think of you up there with the executives."

We couldn't get away from Marcella.

I asked if there was anything different about the Book Section these days.

"Not much," Ollie said. "You have to work harder, that's all. All the stores have the same merchandise now, so you have to get your business from extra knowledge, extra service, extra-wide assortment. I just go pounding what the boss taught: no trouble too great to track down a volume and every clerk must know about the books he's selling. We don't do our own display any more, you know," she confided. "It's all got very fancy. Now it's handled by the Display Department, if you please. We don't even arrange our own books, and we used to switch Juvenile, Fiction, Biography from one end to the other of the section, if the boss had a sudden idea we could sell more that way. We'd work all night. Now we have conferences, requisitions, and approvals before we can change anything."

"And do you remember the hurly-burly we went through on our ads? Well now, my dear, they're planned two months in advance. In a conference again, if you please."

Harriet broke in. "It's more impersonal than it was, and yet in another way it's just as individual as it used to be. Only it's so much bigger. The executives can't get around the way they used to. Why, you remember how Simpson, Yates and Shedd used to go down through the store every day? Well I got a silver tray last year for thirty years' service here. I guess that will set you back. It did me. Anyway, they had a little ceremony and I took it from an executive I'd never seen before. That couldn't have happened in the old days."

I had a sudden, vivid recollection, and told them about a time when Mr. Simpson had sent for me and taken me down to the Rug Section to talk to a saleswoman there who'd been in the department fifty years that day. Mr. Simpson had brought her some flowers and the three of us had sat on a pile of rugs while he chatted with her, asking her questions, drawing out of her anecdotes, experiences she'd had during her years in the store. On the way back to the ninth floor, he'd said to me, "Those are the important people."

"I guess the boss knew as many people in the store as Mr. Simpson did," was Ollie's comment. "She felt the same way about them too."

We made plans to meet again, the three of us, for lunch or cocktails. Marcella, I knew, would be there too. I left her with the others in Ollie's office.

Jean Schureman was the next on my list of people I wanted especially to see. I didn't have to look for him along the aisles of the China Department nor sneak with him behind a display table where we could gossip without being discovered as we'd done in the old days. He was in his office that bore the label, "Vice-

President, General Merchandise Manager." But he was just as pleased to talk about the store and the people in it as if we were again evading the watchful eye of his boss for a little relaxing gossip.

He settled back in his chair and asked if I'd ever heard about the time he'd sold a Lennox dinner set to the wife of a gangster, Hymie Weiss. I told him I hadn't. "Well," he said, "they came in one afternoon at five o'clock. He was as nervous as a cat. Kept looking around him all the time. She went straight over to that set. It was behind glass. It was the only one we had and the most expensive. She pointed to it. Hymie asked if that was the one she wanted. She said it was. Before I had time even to open the case and put a piece of it in his hand to examine, Hymie had a roll out of his pocket and was peeling off bills. 'Wrap it up and send it,' he said, and he handed me Twenty-three Hundred Dollars in cash."

We reminisced a few minutes about the people we'd known. And then I asked about the present day. I'd just heard, I said, that the executives didn't go through the store as much as our bosses had toured it.

"Lord," he said, "I'll never forget the way Simpson used to come through our section with Corley. Simpson would run his fingers over a counter. If he found dust, he'd show his hand to Corley. Corely would rub his hand over the counter and show it to the section head who was following nervously behind. He would do the same thing, and this would go ditto all down the line until the person responsible caught the signal, and, later, hell."

"It's true," he went on, "we don't any of us get around the way those fellows did. Just the same we know the merchandise and the people in the store as well as they ever did. I'd take a bet on that. That's one reason Nutting and I—he's Vice-President and General Manager, you'll meet him, he's since your time—that's why," he repeated, "we have our offices over here instead of with the other executives in the Store for Men. So we can be available to Buyers, Section Managers and get around in the store."

I asked if the Buyers still functioned as independently as in my day.

Jean was emphatic that they did. "They spend one-third of their time buying and two-thirds selling. That's the ratio determined by our store policy. Just as it's our policy they have to buy the merchandise they sell. If it's done for them, we feel they haven't the same initiative to prove their purchase. They could alibi the merchandise was given them; they didn't want it. Every Buyer here is an individual merchant."

I suddenly remembered Mr. Tracy, the Perfume Buyer, and asked Jean about him.

"Gone," he said, "couldn't take the nationally advertised products overrunning his section and doing their own advertising. Even though we hold down that national cosmetics advertising space lower than anybody. But Tracy's got a business as representative of all perfumes and cosmetics not nationally advertised. That's how independent he is."

I asked if Field's still had a Blue Rose perfume since Marshall Field & Company's wholesale was gone.

Jean said they hadn't, but assured me I could probably find something else with just as noxious a name and scent.

When he said good-by, Jean added, "It's funny to think about you doing a book on those days. I remember in the section when girls like you were first coming in. We used to say, 'If a girl says coming to Field's to take a job is amusing, she's writing a book.' And we always used to refer to them as 'book girls.' But none of them ever did write a book, and you never thought the job was amusing."

Jean took me to Mr. Nutting's office and left me there. Mr. Nutting and I talked about the store today, since we had no shared memories.

[ 268 ]

"But," he protested, "don't think I haven't heard about those days. I'll bet I know almost as much about them as if I'd been there myself then."

I told him I didn't doubt that for a minute because one of the first things I'd discovered at Field's was that any employee of five years' standing or over was the original Ancient Mariner in his determination to tell anyone and everyone his story about the store.

"But," I added, "it ought to be a comfort to you to know *I'm* not going to tell you. I'm writing it and that leaves you a choice."

He endorsed what Jean had said about the Buyers. "We send out more people," was Mr. Nutting's assertion, "than any other store, and in Paris we buy more French models than any store in the country. We still believe in individual and unusual merchandise, and we go out for it. But there's one big change since your day. The national products have become so advertised, we have to carry those more than we ever did before, because customers ask for them by name. That takes away a little of our individuality, but it's not of our doing."

"The organization is bigger," he went on. "The top structure is heavier than it was. The management level is more complicated than when you were here. It had to grow with the business, that's all."

In the afternoon I visited the Advertising Bureau. I would never have known it. Standing at the entrance to a long corridor with offices on either side, a switchboard with an operator, a research librarian, so the title on her door defined her, a laboratory with motion-picture screen set up for displaying proposed advertising.

I could only think, "Lawk-a-mercy, this is none of I."

I met Mr. Lawrence B. Sizer, Divisional Vice-President, Sales Promotion Manager, Mr. Gore, Advertising Manager, Mr. Moss, Design Manager, Miss Scott, Special Events Manager, and Mr. Guldager, Public Relations Manager, and I was dazed.

I talked with Mr. Sizer and Mr. Guldager, finding them both possessed of that mark Field's seems still to put on its employees, the teakettle-bubbling enthusiasm. Mr. Sizer was as wonderstruck as a boy by the rare and unusual merchandise in the store.

"We send our people everywhere to get it," he declared, adding eagerly, "Did you know we have the largest collection of English china in the world? And have you seen our collection of paperweights?"

Mr. Guldager told me Field's takes part in civic events to a far greater degree than in my day. Fashion shows, putting on the shows and carrying the whole expense for these; flower shows, debutante cotillions for hospital benefits. He cited, too, the fifteen departments in the store exclusively for services, from checking packages, to checking children in a supervised nursery.

I was giddy when I had to leave them to keep my appointment with Mr. McBain. We agreed to meet again the following day.

Mr. McBain's secretary told me he was waiting and invited me to go right in. He was sitting at his desk when I opened the door, but he met me halfway across the room. We shook hands.

He hadn't changed much from the young man outside Mr. Simpson's office who'd been kind to me each time I'd nervously answered the summons of an executive.

I hadn't thought then, I told him as we walked together back to his desk, about his being Chairman of the Board one day. He hadn't himself, he said and grinned. He'd been too busy. Simpson had kept him hopping.

I sat down in the chair he indicated beside the desk and we talked about old times and the men who were the executives then. Mr. Shedd he considered the greatest merchant and the best developer of men; 1900 to 1920 the period of greatest growth in the store.

"But Selfridge," he added quickly, "gave this store its personality. He was the P. T. Barnum."

He reverted to Mr. Shedd. "A great man for quality," he repeated and smiled, "but very tight about money. I remember," Mr. McBain continued, "one time when he was in California— I was his secretary then—I mailed him from the store a copy of *The American Magazine*. It had in it an article on Selfridge. I thought he'd be interested to read it. Shedd wrote back, thanking me, but said I could have cut out the article and mailed it with a letter for two cents, instead of paying six cents for the whole magazine."

"Simpson," Mr. McBain resumed, "was a financier, not a merchant. He was a genius for figures. As a person he was cold. Actually, he was a shy man. He had very few friends in business, whereas Shedd had a great many."

"Shedd used to go through the store, jump up on the cases in the sections and sit there chatting with the Buyers. You'd never have found Simpson doing that."

He broke off to ask if I'd been talking to people about the store today. I told him I had, and had heard again and again that it was still based on the individual.

Mr. McBain said, "This is a Buyer's store. Always has been and always will be. A Marshall Field Buyer's signature on an order is all that's necessary. It doesn't have to be approved or countersigned by anyone."

He waved his hand around his office. I hadn't noticed before that there was merchandise of almost every description, on shelves and over chairs: a rug, a piece of china, some glass, pottery bowls, bolts of fabric, a bamboo curtain. I couldn't take them all in. I looked back inquiringly at Mr. McBain.

"Samples," he said, "from foreign trips. Every time a Buyer gets back, I have him up here just as quick as I can to tell me all about his trip, and as soon as the stuff comes, I get a sample of everything that's been purchased. This is a Buyer-run store," he repeated. "Up here we're just the impresarios. And what they bring back to sell here is fascinating to me. I never want Marshall Field's to curtail their Buyers or their markets."

Shortly after that I left.

On my way out a secretary stopped me. "Did he happen to tell you," she asked, nodding in the direction of Mr. McBain's office, "why he had to put off his appointment with you this morning?"

"Why, no," I said, "it was perfectly all right."

"Well," she continued, "you might be interested to know. It

seems last night he and Mrs. McBain were out to dinner and an old lady there told him she was disappointed in Field's because a package she'd ordered hadn't been delivered. And she'd always understood Field's was the one store where every article purchased went out that same day.

"Mr. McBain said he'd see about it. He's always being asked things like that, you know. Every time he goes out it's just terrible."

"I know," I interrupted, "at least, I remember."

"Well, anyway," she continued, "this morning the first thing when he came in, he went down to the section where the old lady had made her purchase. He found the article had had to be specially ordered and had just come in. So, you know what he did? He sent for his car and took the package out to her house on the North Shore. And then he came back to work again. That's why he couldn't see you. He was late getting his second start."

I retraced my steps across the secretary's office and tapped on Mr. McBain's door.

He called, "Come in."

I opened and stuck my head around it. "When you delivered that parcel this morning, what did you say?"

He looked at me, startled for a moment and then he grinned. "Package from Field's," he answered.

Charley would have liked that.